MW01060945

EMBODYING HEALING:

Integrating Bodywork
and Psychotherapy
in Recovery from
Childhood Sexual Abuse

Robert J. Timms, Ph.D.
Patrick Connors, C.M.T.

Foreword: Christine A. Courtois, Ph.D.

The Safer Society Press
Shoreham Depot Road
RR #1, Box 24B
Orwell, Vermont 05760-9756

Library of Congress Number 92–082849

Appendix A reprinted with permission from the author, Carlos Loredo, Ph.D., Austin, Texas.

Cover Design: Maureen Burgess

Editor: Euan Bear

Order from:

The Safer Society Press
RR 1, Box 24–B
Orwell, VT 05760–9756
(802) 897–7541

1–4 copies ....$15.00 each, includes shipping
5–9 copies ....$15.00 each, plus $2.50 shipping
10–24 copies ....$12.00 each, plus 5% shipping
25 or more ....$10.50 each, plus 5% shipping

ALL ORDERS MUST BE PREPAID, U.S. FUNDS ONLY.
Vermont residents please add sales tax.

DEDICATION

This book is respectfully dedicated to all persons, men and women, girls and boys, who have been (and unfortunately, those who yet will be) sexually abused in childhood. The pain of such abuse, though terrible, can be relieved and resolved. We are pleased to offer to survivors and to their therapists an approach to treatment that we hope will bring increased embodiment and greater healing for all.

ACKNOWLEDGEMENTS

We gladly take this opportunity to acknowledge people who have made significant contributions in the formation and completion of this book.

Let's start with Fay Honey Knopp. From our initial meeting in Minneapolis at the first Male Survivor Conference in 1988, Honey has been totally supportive of us and encouraging of our work. It is a gift to know Honey and an honor to work with her.

Getting to know Euan Bear has been one of the most treasured and unexpected blessings of this project. Her skills as an editor have been surpassed only by her compassion, love, and understanding as a friend.

We had the good fortune to spend a week in Vermont this summer working on this book, and Rob Freeman–Longo, along with the entire staff of The Safer Society Program and Press, helped make it a memorable working vacation. Burt Knopp is an extraordinary person and a most gracious and entertaining host.

Thanks and respect are due all those persons who have participated in our workshops over the years. Their questions and comments have given us valuable feedback and helped us look more closely at ourselves and our work. We also appreciate Mic Hunter, who gave our model its first published exposure.

Appreciation is due Theresa Bacon, Ben Benjamin, Ph.D., William Coil, N.C.M.T., Jacque Damgaard, Ph.D., Robert Green, M.A., C.C.M.H.C., Lory Skwerer, and Walter Zeichner, M.A., all of whom graciously took time to review this book in manuscript and offer comments, criticisms, and suggestions.

Special thanks go to Christine A. Courtois, Ph.D., who wrote the Foreword to this book. Not only is she a knowledgeable and eloquent writer on sexual abuse, she is also a strong advocate for empowering abuse survivors. Her thoughtful recognition, support, and encouragement of our work is deeply gratifying and most appreciated.

The many clients who shared their pain and growth with us contributed significantly to our writing of this book. We are honored by their trust in allowing us to be part of their recovery from childhood sexual abuse. We wish them all continued health and happiness.

This book is intended for psychotherapists working with survivors of childhood sexual and/or physical abuse who want to add bodywork to the therapeutic process; for bodyworkers who want to know more about therapeutic work with abuse survivors; and, of course, for survivors themselves. We have decided to spell out some of the features of this therapeutic work rather than make assumptions about what each person involved in the treatment process might already know. Our intention is to establish some common base of knowledge for everyone involved in the healing process of facilitating the survivor's recovery.

Many psychotherapists have been reluctant to explore the benefits of touch in therapy with survivors; this book provides a structured approach to therapeutic touch that addresses some of their concerns. Many bodyworkers want to work more fully with abuse survivors and to know more about the psychological dynamics of abuse. We hope that the Psychophysical Model described in this book will facilitate effective professional collaboration between bodyworkers and psychotherapists.

The therapeutic introduction of touch into work with survivors often intensifies therapeutic issues. Similarly, talking about uses of touch in psychotherapy may produce intense reactions for some therapists. Therapeutic orientation and personality play significant roles in how a psychotherapist views touch in the therapeutic process. We do not pretend our approach works for all clients; nor will it be acceptable to all psychotherapists. We offer this book as one voice in a continuing conversation on an important topic in recovery, knowing there will be many different reactions. We hope that psychotherapists who may be predisposed to discount or disapprove of the use of touch in therapy will be open to the experiences of the many clients across the country who have on their own initiative sought out massage and other types of bodywork and found these modalities helpful and healing.

In addition to theory, we offer some guidelines for collaborative practice and some case examples for illustration. All cases are from our practices, real persons whose names and other identifying information have been changed to protect confidentiality. We deeply value the work of these clients and appreciate their willingness to share their stories in this book.

We take this opportunity to acknowledge and encourage survivors who are seeking additional avenues of growth for their full recovery from childhood abuse. Some have already intuitively found bodywork to be important in their healing; others may want to share this book with their therapists as a way of beginning to explore whether and how to incorporate therapeutic touching into their current process.

TABLE OF CONTENTS

FOREWORD

Studies of trauma have documented that it involves and impacts the whole person: body, mind, and emotions. To quote authors Robert Timms and Patrick Connors, "Emotional trauma has a physical impact; physical trauma carries an emotional impact." Whether psychological or emotional, trauma is shocking and overwhelming. It stresses the individual and causes both psychological and physiological disequilibrium and dysregulation. These effects vary in intensity and degree according to characteristics of the trauma and to the individual's resiliency, that is, the capacity to withstand or cope with such traumatic stress.

Child sexual abuse is a unique type of trauma. It involves intimate transgression, directed at and involving the victim's body and sexuality in some way. Most commonly, the victim's body is the locus of the abuse which involves touch, violation, and penetration and which might cause pain, discomfort, and stimulation, alone or in combination. Even when sexual abuse does not involve touch (in the case of voyeurism and/or exhibitionism), the victim's body or response may be fetishized and debased. Sexual abuse is a deliberate, premeditated, human–induced violation to fulfill the needs of the perpetrator for power and control. In the usual case, the perpetrator is related or known to the child and uses the relationship to gain access and compliance. Once involved, the child is cautioned or threatened to keep the abuse secret, an entrapping circumstance that allows for the intensification of the abuse over time. The child caught in such a situation is hard–pressed to escape physically and often must resort to psychological escape via the defense mechanisms of denial, dissociation, repression, and amnesia, which counter the intolerable emotional and physical reactions that accompany the abuse.

Although the victim may make a psychological escape, the body is left "holding the bag," so to speak. The body is the repository for what the mind forgets when the traumatic events and their associated emotions are encoded at the biochemical and neuromuscular levels. The emotions most often associated with abuse include but are not limited to shame, humiliation, guilt, anger, depression, fear and anxiety, betrayal and confusion, despair, mistrust, and grief. These emotions might also be expressed behaviorally and relationally as well as physically, all intertwined in a complex relationship. Physical responses and manifestations can be quite variable but often include chronic muscle tension (body armoring), postural distortion, a limited range of motion, somatic–visceral response, sexual distress, chronic hyperalertness and other stress symptoms, illness and disease, somatization, distortions of body perception, and fears associated with touch and body sensations.

To date, researchers and clinicians have focused almost exclusively on the psychological aftermath of sexual abuse and paid little or no attention to its physical effects and manifestations. Consequently, treatment efforts have followed suit. With *Embodying Healing*, psychotherapist Robert Timms and massage therapist Patrick Connors break new ground in the treatment of survivors of child sexual abuse. In their Psychophysical Model standard psychological techniques are enhanced and/or accelerated by bodywork and an emphasis on the physical domain. The body, too, needs help to offset the lessons and the damage of the abuse.

In the bodywork component of treatment, body awareness is an end in and of itself. Touch is relearned and the body reclaimed and restored from the violation of the abuse. Body image improves as this new learning contradicts shame and other abuse–related emotions. Additionally, because bodywork bypasses both cognitive processes and psychological defenses and often produces an altered state of consciousness, it creates a circumstance in which previously repressed or dissociated memory may return to consciousness.

Bodywork thus becomes a powerful adjunct to talk and insight-focused therapy. The authors are respectful of the potency of this model and take pains to incorporate it within accepted guidelines for the treatment of adult survivors of child sexual abuse. They detail a structure for collaborative treatment by the psychotherapist and bodyworker with carefully spelled–out professional roles and responsibilities. They are well aware of the need for paced and titrated individually–tailored treatment of survivors and offer a clear protocol with attention to boundaries, limitations, and privacy. The survivor-client is empowered through consultation, inclusion in treatment planning, and control of timing and content.

Timms and Connors know the efficacy of this model through their collaborative work with survivors but, more compellingly, through their personal experience providing and receiving such treatment. They both have firsthand experience regarding its healing potential, as they document in their introduction. They are to be congratulated for their courage in sharing their personal experience and for developing it into a model of treatment for use by other professionals. *Embodying Healing* advances the healing options and techniques for practitioners working with the myriad effects of child sexual abuse.

— ***Christine A. Courtois, Ph.D.,***
Psychologist, Private Practice;
Clinical Director, Center for
Abuse Recovery & Empowerment;
Author, *Healing The Incest Wound:*
Adult Survivors in Therapy

INTRODUCTION

Major changes can happen suddenly. One afternoon in the summer of 1987, I entered my third massage session with a 46–year–old male client who wanted to reduce his blood pressure, his stress level, and his weight. During the massage, he recalled, with considerable pain and tears, a totally forgotten event from his childhood: at the age of six he had been attacked and raped by his favorite uncle. I had never experienced a session like this before. By the end of the hour, I knew I would never approach a massage session in the same way again. I was amazed that such powerful memories and emotions could be stored in the body for 40 years and be unavailable to the conscious mind. I was surprised and confused that he could have been amnesic about so traumatic an incident. Most importantly, I was moved by the pure emotionality of the experience, and I struggled with feelings of inadequacy in not knowing how to help my client work with his emotions. Instinct, intention, and intuition are powerful tools and provide a great starting place, yet I became acutely aware of my limitations in doing the work that was so important to me.

—*Patrick Connors*, Certified Massage Therapist

I was the client with whom Patrick worked that fateful day. In 10 years of personal psychotherapy with excellent therapists, I had never before recalled being sexually abused in childhood. The memory produced in that massage session was a powerful and emotional discovery for me. For the first time, many aspects of my life made total sense. With this new knowledge of an old memory guiding my psychotherapy, I was able to make considerable personal gains in growth and change, including losing 40 pounds, lowering my blood pressure, and decreasing my feelings of depression. I also gained the capacity to feel happiness, health, and a sense of new possibilities for being fully engaged in my own life.

I would like to take this opportunity to acknowledge Patrick for the major role he played in my recovery from childhood abuse. I would also like to say to other survivors that similar help for a happier future is available to them.

—*Robert J. Timms, Ph.D.*, Clinical Psychologist

We both considered that in addition to the personal benefit Bob obtained from his bodywork, this type of professional bodywork experience could help Bob's psychotherapy clients. We discussed this concept and almost immediately started developing ideas how to integrate bodywork into psychotherapy with abuse survivors and other clients. We made use of our own personal experiences and learnings as the basis for developing our new clinical ideas, as have many clinicians and theorists, such as Reich, Alexander, Perls, Feldenkreis, and Lowen and Pierrakos (who did bodywork with each other in developing Bioenergetics; see Lowen, 1975, pp. 37–42). This book tells what we learned and how we developed our practice and work, in hopes that it will help other psychotherapists, bodyworkers, and survivors collaborate successfully in this effective healing process.

1

Sexual Abuse:
The Secret Revealed
in Body and Mind

Since 1980, mental health professionals have learned much about identifying and treating adult survivors of childhood sexual abuse. Psychotherapeutic approaches have proliferated, with attention given to healing the child within and restoring the survivor to healthy adult functioning. While most of these approaches acknowledge the physical impact of abuse on the body, much less attention has been given to treating the trauma's impact at a physical level. In this book, we present our view that childhood sexual abuse affects the whole person, body, mind, and spirit. Such abuse ripples through the survivor's adult life, affecting thought, emotional feeling, physical sensation, and behavior. The trauma affects all these areas, and they must all be addressed in treatment. To this end, we propose an integrated treatment approach that attends to the physical as well as to the emotional trauma of childhood sexual abuse: the Psychophysical Model.

Childhood sexual abuse is a widespread problem in our society. It is perpetrated upon an alarming number of young females and males every year. Depending on the definition of abuse used, estimates range from one in seven to one in three females, and from one in ten to one in four males (Crewdson, 1988; Finkelhor, 1984). Research indicates young females are more likely to be abused by a family member, while young males are more likely to be abused by a friend, acquaintance, or stranger outside the home (Abel, Mittelman, & Becker, 1983). Sexual abuse covers a wide range of inappropriate behaviors, including voyeurism (peeping), exhibitionism (flashing), invasive touching (fondling), and oral, anal, and vaginal contact.

It is difficult to conceptualize or explain why some abuse survivors show more severe consequences of childhood trauma than do others. Therapist Jan Hindman (1989) is very clear about the complexities of defining and evaluating childhood sexual abuse, and the multiple interaction of factors that lead to traumatic consequences in adult life. She compares typical legal definitions of abuse severity (four factors: early onset, use of violence, frequency of occurrence, and penetration) with a new nine–factor paradigm based on her own research with adult victims. According to Hindman (1989, pp. 77–88,) nine factors correlating to *severe* traumatic effects on victims of childhood sexual abuse include:

1. any *sexual responsiveness* by the victim;
2. *terror* related to how long the victim spent knowing an assault would take place at a particular time (*anticipation,* not overt violence);
3. the victim's *inability clearly to identify the offender as responsible* for the offense (often the result of "tenderness" and "nurturing" behavior by the perpetrator, or related to a "hypocrisy index" where the higher the perpetrator's status within the family and the community, the more trauma for the victim);
4. the victim's *inability to identify himself or herself as the victim* (usually the result of perpetrator messages blaming the victim, such as "you made me do this");
5. *onset of sexual abuse under age 12* (related to developmental stage, i.e., each developmental stage still to come represents an opportunity for the memory and meaning of the sexual abuse to be distorted);
6. "footprints," such as *denial, rationalization, or minimization;*
7. *withheld report* (secrecy);
8. *disastrous response* by family members or other significant individuals;
9. *trauma bond,* the continued demand for relationship with the perpetrator.

The common belief that sexual abuse involving penetration is "worse" or results in more trauma in adulthood than sexual abuse involving fondling does not hold true. What some persons might refer to as "mere fondling" may lead to painful and severe adult consequences for some survivors. Further, "covert" forms of child sexual abuse frequently lead to strong adult feelings of shame, guilt, and fear. The common element we see in trauma is betrayal: the more severe the degree of betrayal of trust, the greater the psychological damage to the child, and the more trauma for the adult survivor.

Therapists must be especially careful not to minimize the effect or compare any client's memory of abusive touching, regardless of content. While trauma may be present in varying degrees, there is no such thing as "minor" sexual abuse. Abuse is abuse, no matter what form it takes. All survivors of any form of sexual abuse who choose to undergo the difficult process of reliving memories and re–experiencing painful feelings show incredible courage.[1]

Sexual abuse of children, whether by peer–age children, older children, or by adults, is an invasion of the child's physical and emotional life. Child sexual abuse occurs within a relationship in which the other person exerts power and control (both real and perceived) over the victim. A relationship in which sexual behavior is forced on a person by someone with more power is not a peer relationship or a relationship of choice. Healthy and appro-

---

[1] For a concise, thorough, and compassionate exploration of the survivor experience, see *Adults Molested as Children: A Survivor's Manual for Women and Men* (Bear & Dimock, 1988).

priate sexuality can exist only in a peer relationship that respects choice and allows true consent.[2]

Because sexual abuse occurs within the context of an interpersonal relationship, the abuse colors the child's later perceptions of other interpersonal situations. The survivor may become passive, fearful, and acquiescent in future relationships. Other survivors may overcompensate by becoming aggressive, seeking to control people by any means rather than ever again feeling controlled.

Not all adult survivors remember being abused. For some, survival was possible only by forgetting, resulting in partial or complete amnesia about the abuse. This experience of immediate amnesia and its relationship to the phenomenon of dissociation will be discussed more fully in Chapter 3.

The repression of memories of the abuse by some survivors may be related to the abuser's threats. Abused children are commonly told by abusers that great harm, even death, will come to them, their pets, or family members if they tell anyone about the abuse. Many survivors keep the abuse secret until they are adults, telling no one during childhood. Keeping such a significant secret requires the expenditure of considerable mental and/or psychic energy and leads to adult manifestations of secret-keeping that may show up as somatic symptoms of stress or physical illness. When children do tell and are not believed, they learn negative, distorted, and untrue messages about themselves that may also be expressed somatically, especially chronic muscular tension or "armoring." They learn to doubt themselves and to distrust their own perceptions of reality, affecting everything from whether an event happened to what they are really feeling in their bodies.

Denial and dissociation are two defense mechanisms, or coping strategies, that allow the child to survive. Two forms of denial are denying that the abuse happened, and denying the significance and consequences of acknowledged abuse in the survivor's adult life.

Dissociation, the sense of leaving one's body, can be a strong protection by allowing the survivor to separate from the immediacy of a painful emotional or physical memory by feeling confused, spaced out, or numb.

Because of the mechanisms of denial and dissociation, it is not unusual for an adult abuse survivor to enter psychotherapy with a variety of emotional and physical issues and not mention a history of abuse. Physical issues may include chronic headaches, chronic pain in various parts of the body, digestive distress, eating disorders, sleep disturbances, hypertension, alcohol and drug abuse, and sexual difficulties.

---

[2] The National Task Force on Juvenile Sexual Offending (1988) defines *consent* as including all of the following six components: 1) understanding the proposed action based on both participants' age, maturity, developmental level, physical condition, and experience; 2) knowing society's standards for the proposed action; 3) being aware of the potential consequences of this action and alternatives to it; 4) being certain that the participants' choices to agree or disagree will be equally respected; 5) deciding voluntarily, without coercion of any kind; 6) knowing that both participants are mentally competent to make this decision at this time (p. 8).

Sexual dysfunctions and/or compulsive sexual behaviors are common among adult survivors, both female and male. Though often initially reluctant to discuss it, many male survivors have sexual difficulties including impotence, premature ejaculation, or delayed orgasm. Women survivors may have difficulty experiencing orgasm or have vaginal pain that precludes sexual pleasure. Both male and female survivors frequently experience shame associated with sexual behavior and/or may sometimes act out in sexually inappropriate ways.

For some survivors, sexual behavior in adult life may be expressed in either extreme sexual inhibition or pronounced sexual promiscuity (Timms & Connors, 1992). Sexual inhibition defends against any possible re–enactment of the abuse within a sexual framework. Promiscuity may reflect unconsciously motivated re–enactments of the abuse, repeated in hopes of achieving a different outcome. These extremes are two among several self–destructive behavior patterns that adult survivors may be involved in when they first enter therapy.

When survivors are amnesic about abuse, it is impossible for them to connect the childhood abuse they experienced to their dysfunctional behavior in adulthood. However, even when a client does remember the abuse, she or he may not see any connection between the abuse and current physical, emotional, or behavioral concerns. Part of the therapist's job is to help the client discover these connections.

Development of physical symptoms or interference with adult sexual behavior are only two ways childhood abuse disrupts normal adult life. The experience of sexual abuse fundamentally affects its victims' relationships: business and personal; with other males, other females, perhaps even with children; and, most basically, with the self.

The impact of childhood trauma can create a negative physical self–image as well as a negative emotional one. Abuse survivors often have an unrealistic sense of their bodies, that is, how they see and feel themselves to be is often incongruent with how other people see them. For example, some survivors may work out rigorously and regularly at the gym, yet still see themselves as weak, overweight, or inadequately developed. Further, abuse survivors may have difficulty in distinguishing physical stimuli accurately, resulting in a high tolerance for pain (due to dissociation) or hypersensitivity to touch. Sometimes a gentle touch feels more intimidating or intrusive than a stronger, firmer touch. These issues have a direct impact on how psychotherapists and bodyworkers use the Psychophysical Model with survivors of sexual abuse and will be discussed in more detail in Chapter 3.

It is not unusual for abuse survivors to have some form of eating disorder.[3] Some survivors may gain weight as a protective mechanism, a way of insulating themselves further from potential abusers. Survivors of any size may use food as their drug of choice to avoid painful emotions, or they may be bulimic or anorexic. Along with food abuse, other forms of substance abuse

---

[3] One eating disorder treatment center has reported that of 100 consecutive patients seen, 61 percent reported incidents of sexual abuse that occurred prior to age 18 (Miller, 1991).

such as alcohol or drugs are also frequently found in survivors. A realistic body image that includes self–awareness and self–acceptance is a therapeutic goal.[4]

Abuse survivors face other health risks, including hypertension (particularly in males), migraines, a higher risk of cervical cancer for women (when sexual abuse included intercourse before age 16; American Cancer Society, 1992, 1990), and reported higher rates of physical dysfunction of the reproductive system in women with a history of sexual abuse in childhood (personal communication from Atlanta–based gynecologist William McKenzie, M.D., July 9, 1992).

Healing Both Body and Mind

In sexual abuse, the body is involved: it is invaded, its value distorted; it is used, made into a vehicle for physical pain, unwanted or confusing sexual responses, or dissociative absence. In a sense, the survivor's body, or at least the survivor's comfort and ease with his or her body, was stolen. *Since the body was integral to the trauma, it must be integrated into the healing process.*

Survivors often need help to reclaim their bodies from the experience of abuse. To help survivors reclaim their bodies, and in some cases recapture repressed memories for reprocessing, we have developed a treatment approach we call the Psychophysical Model. This approach to therapy is based on our own personal and professional experiences (Timms & Connors, 1990). It combines hands–on bodywork and verbal psychotherapy to increase the effectiveness of treatment and shorten the recovery process. In our model, the bodywork is done by an appropriately trained massage therapist, and an experienced professional psychotherapist provides the psychotherapy.[5] Throughout this book we use the terms "bodyworker" and "massage therapist" interchangeably.

Two major features of our model contribute to its therapeutic effectiveness. First, the combination of bodywork and psychotherapy greatly facilitates the retrieval of repressed traumatic memories by drawing upon "muscle memory" (discussed in detail in Chapter 3). Second, a coordinated treatment approach offers the client *two* sets of professional skills; neither therapist crosses professional boundaries or works outside his or her areas of expertise. Maintaining clear boundaries and respecting the client–therapist relationship (discussed in Chapter 7) are always important, and particularly when working with survivors of childhood sexual abuse.

Before treatment, many survivors develop a style of life based on protection, compensation, and distortion. Whatever cognitive distortions were necessary for the child to survive can become solidified into adult reality.

---

[4] Therapists should never assume that a client who verbally presents her/his weight as an issue, or who is diagnosed with an eating disorder, is an abuse survivor; nor should it ever be assumed that a heavy client either has an eating disorder or is an abuse survivor.

[5] See Appendix A for suggested guidelines and questions for clients on choosing a psychotherapist, and Appendix B for suggestions on how a client working outside a formally structured therapeutic collaboration might choose a bodyworker.

Betrayal by a loved and trusted family member or close friend undermines and skews the child's whole conceptual life foundation.

This betrayal of trust produces a double bind for the child: a dependence on the abusing person for food, shelter, protection, love, and/or attention coupled with pain, manipulation, and humiliation. This double bind can be endured only by unconscious and protective repression of deep emotions and memories, resulting in profound internal conflict and problems later in life. During and after the trauma the child does everything possible to keep himself or herself together and to function as well as possible in the world: the child survives.

Children abused by people outside the family (neighbors, coaches, teachers, classmates, or total strangers) carry their own unique emotional scars. Their double–bind is a constant war between their natural curiosity about the world around them and their abuse–fostered hypervigilance. Abused children see the world only as dangerous and threatening, a place where anyone new is a menace, where the urge to explore, to connect with people, is suffocated by the betrayal of the abuser.

Usually, survivors find ways to compensate. One survivor may excel in school to receive positive attention and to remove himself or herself from the painful family situation, while another may develop athletic prowess as a way to feel safe and accepted. Yet another may retreat inward because the external world is unsafe, developing an intense personal fantasy life in order to survive the abuse. In adulthood, survivors may compensate in such culturally accepted (though stereotypic) ways as by becoming workaholics or trying to be "Super-Mom" or "SuperDad." Though varied, all these efforts represent different survival strategies. As a therapist, one can only marvel at the variety of creative strategies survivors have employed to endure the trauma and bring themselves into adult life, where healing can finally be available.

Basically, the adult consequences of childhood abuse are such that the survivor's defenses begin to break down or interfere with adult functioning in a job or relationship. Life can feel like a time bomb. The survivor is afraid that something is going to explode: a marriage or a relationship breaks up; drug or alcohol abuse become problematic; or life becomes intolerable and suicide appears as a serious option. While survivors may enter therapy presenting one or more of these issues and *initially* may not identify a history of sexual abuse, the fact remains that their lives are being affected by the physical, emotional, and mental trauma of childhood sexual abuse.

Verbal therapy alone is not necessarily the most effective treatment. Talking about what happened, even with emotions, leaves the physical experience of abuse unresolved. While the necessity of healing and reframing the mental and emotional aspects of abuse is generally acknowledged, it is equally necessary to reframe and heal the physical components. The more holistic the treatment approach, the more effective it can be.

A Brief Outline of the Psychophysical Model

The Psychophysical Model is a combination of active, verbal psychotherapy and hands–on bodywork using collaboration between a psychotherapist and a massage therapist. It promotes integrated healing for clients suffering the effects of emotional, physical, and/or sexual trauma.

The Psychophysical Model is not appropriate for all clients. The psychotherapist and client together must evaluate whether and when the client might be helped by psychophysical therapy (see Chapter 3 for criteria). When the psychotherapist ascertains that a client can benefit from bodywork or when the question of bodywork is brought up by the client, the Psychophysical Model is introduced into the therapy process.

The psychotherapist explains how bodywork might help the client and solicits and responds to the client's reactions. The client receives a handout (see Appendix C) describing what can be expected in a bodywork session. If and when both the therapist and the client agree the time is right, the bodyworker is introduced to the client during the next psychotherapy session.

During this verbal introductory session (in which no bodywork occurs) the client meets the bodyworker and discloses as much of his or her abuse history as is comfortable. The client also discusses with the bodyworker his or her perceptions of the psychotherapeutic work up to this time. The client, the psychotherapist, and the bodyworker together set appropriate goals for their future collaborative therapy. The client signs a form authorizing the psychotherapist and the bodyworker to discuss the client's case and progress (see Appendix D), and the client is given a brief medical history form to fill out and return to the bodyworker (see Appendix E).

Any questions about or reactions to the bodywork handout are addressed in this session. Typical questions concern fears about being touched, whether or not the client will need to undress, or the client's fear of having a sexual reaction to the bodywork. These normal concerns are honestly and respectfully addressed in order to lower the client's anxiety level and to build the trust necessary to allow the bodywork to succeed. We have found that a simple, direct, nonjudgmental answer to a direct question is the most effective response.

Since most survivors have trust issues and are accustomed to keeping secrets, both professionals must make very clear that the psychotherapist and the bodyworker—with the client's written permission—will periodically discuss their collaboration on the client's treatment. This communication is necessary for both therapists to have access to the full information being provided by the client as well as to counter the two therapists' susceptibility to being "split" in reaction to client feedback.[6] Explaining the nature of the team approach usually resolves any questions.

In working with the client using the Psychophysical Model, two different modes are possible: sequential and combined. In both modes, the client is in ongoing psychotherapy and also receives massage therapy on a regular basis. In the sequential mode, the client has a massage therapy session immediately followed by a psychotherapy session. By experiencing bodywork just before the psychotherapy session, the client comes to psychotherapy with more body awareness and is usually able to gain access to emotions more readily. He or she is more relaxed and less defended. The client may even regain specific memories, thoughts, images, or feelings during massage therapy that are then processed in the psychotherapy session. Most of our work is done using the sequential mode.

In the combined mode, the massage therapist works with the client physically in the presence of the psychotherapist. The psychotherapist helps the client concentrate on and process emerging feelings and sensations, both physical and emotional.

Clients generally begin by using the sequential mode. After a number of sequential sessions, or when the client has been experiencing intense emotions during several massage therapy sessions, the combined mode is particularly useful. These combined sessions are often very powerful, and some of our clients prefer to continue using only the combined approach.

Therapists should be especially sensitive to gender issues when working with sexual abuse survivors. While many survivors express no gender preference, we support the choices of clients who may be more comfortable at the beginning of their treatment with a psychotherapist and/or bodyworker of their own gender. We firmly believe that at some point in the client's therapy some bodywork needs to occur with a massage therapist who is of the same gender as the abuser. If the original damage was done by a male (as the majority of *reported* abuse is), it is vitally important that a male become a part of the healing, to allow for the completion of accurate adult perception of males. Since not all males are abusers, it is important for a survivor to see that men can also be helpful, healing, nurturing, and caring. Similarly, survivors who were abused by females need at some point to work with a female bodyworker and/or psychotherapist.

The term *bodywork* is used in this book to designate a wide variety of body–centered techniques that may or may not involve physically touching the body. Nontouch bodywork may include any of several guided relaxation techniques (Jacobson's progressive relaxation, for example; see Jacobson, 1938), breathing exercises, or other focusing techniques used to promote bodily

---

[6] "Splitting" in this context occurs when a client relates much more positively to one team member and more negatively to the other, usually as a re–enactment of a family dynamic. The client may ask "the good guy" to keep secret the negative feedback about the "bad guy" (see Chapter 7).

awareness. Hands–on bodywork can include nurturing touch with gentle massage strokes on the superficial layers of muscles, a process most clients would probably describe as feeling soothing and calming.

Bodywork also refers to techniques used to manipulate the mid-to-deep layers of muscle and connective tissue. In this type of work the bodyworker focuses on areas of chronic tension (which may have an emotional origin) in an attempt to release the muscular contraction (and perhaps provide a corresponding release of emotion). Some types of active resistance exercises are also considered part of bodywork; for example, the client might push against the bodyworker's hands or shoulders to achieve a sense of empowerment and a realistic perception of his or her adult strength.

Our goal in therapy is to help the client move not only through the victim stage and beyond even the survivor stage. We encourage clients to become *thrivers:* people who actively choose their lives and live with vitality, self–awareness, and self–esteem. Our particular approach to therapy based on a structured collaboration between a psychotherapist and a bodyworker is relatively new. But it continues a body–mind focus based on pre–existing theoretical and practical ideas from psychology and massage therapy. The next chapter reviews the historical and theoretical bases of our work.

2

The Connection Between Psychotherapy and Bodywork: A Brief History

Though our particular form of combining bodywork and psychotherapy is new, therapeutic awareness of the importance of the body in psychotherapy has a long historical background, beginning with Freud and continuing into the present.

Much of Freud's early work was with women who would now be recognized as abuse survivors. At that time, however, they were frequently diagnosed as "hysterical," that is, they had presented physical and emotional symptoms for which no known organic cause could be found. In 1895 and 1896, Freud heard many of the women describe memories of childhood sexual experiences with older men, often their fathers. Freud at first was inclined to believe this testimony, and discussed his perceptions in a paper he presented in 1896 to the Society for Psychiatry and Neurology, in Vienna. The paper was negatively received by his colleagues. It has been suggested that Freud was pressured to suppress his views by his colleagues and by the culture of secrecy and denial concerning intergenerational sex (Masson, 1984). Whether because of this pressure, or for some other reason, Freud developed the theory that such memories were the result of an unresolved Oedipal conflict, reflecting a young girl's desire to be sexual with her father. This theory changed the course of psychotherapeutic work with survivors and placed an intolerable burden of disbelief on the shoulders of survivors that continues to this day. Be that as it may, Freud did contribute some useful concepts related to therapeutic work with abuse survivors.

Freud developed the concept of defense mechanisms, unconscious methods we use to protect ourselves from strong feelings of anxiety. A major example of a defense mechanism is repression. When an event or a memory is too emotionally painful to accept, we unconsciously push it into the background of our minds where it will not bother us, and where we may forget about it entirely. The ability to repress the trauma of childhood sexual abuse serves young persons well. The pain and terror are held back until the survivor has reached an adult state in life and has the social, emotional, and intellectual resources to deal with such childhood memories and feelings. This is one of the reasons why painful memories of childhood trauma often surface when people are in their 30s or 40s. Repression plays a part in denial, discussed in Chapter 4.

Freud (1950, first written in 1929) also stated, "The ego is first and foremost a body ego," adding, "The ego is ultimately derived from bodily sensations" (p. 17). We understand this to mean that the ego, or sense of self, is integrally involved in our bodily emotions, sensations, and experiences. Though Freud did not actively pursue the relationship between body, personal growth, and healing, the location of the ego in the body was a very important theoretical contribution on which many of his followers built their theories.

Georg Groddeck, chronologically a contemporary of Freud, is thought by Lawrence Durrell (in his 1976 preface to Groddeck's *The Book of the It,* first published in 1923) to have been "the only analyst whose views had some effect on Freud," (p. vi) especially on Freud's writing of *The Ego and the Id* (1950). Groddeck was a controversial figure in his time. He held very holistic beliefs about the human body, teaching that our emotions and beliefs find direct and powerful expression in our bodily sensations and health. He attended to such issues as headaches, hypertension, self–destructive behaviors, and sexual dysfunctions. He established a clinic in Baden–Baden where he treated his patients with a combination of diet, deep massage, and psychoanalysis (Groddeck, 1976, p. xiii). His work made a profound impact on Durrell, who wrote in 1948, "No analyst can afford to disregard Groddeck's views about such matters as resistance and transference any more than he can afford to disregard him on questions like ... the relation of analysis to organic disorders, and the uses of massage" (Groddeck, 1976, p. xxiii). Even though Groddeck has been considered by some to be a major developer of the field of psychosomatic medicine from a psychoanalytic perspective, the larger psychoanalytic community chose for some time to disregard his views on the value of physical interventions, including the use of massage.

Both Freud and Groddeck professionally influenced the work of Wilhelm Reich, an Austrian–born psychoanalyst who wrote the influential book *Character Analysis* in 1933. In this book, Reich moved past Freud's theory into a belief that a person's emotional experiences in life *directly* influence the body, appearing in what Reich called "character armor." Reich defined character as "a term signifying typical biophysical behavior" (1972, p. xi).

Character armor, then, is the physical manifestation of what happens when a person behaves in typical, characteristic ways based on repressed emotions. The musculature of the person becomes chronically tight in a way specific to that person's emotional history. The purpose of this muscular tightness is to hold in or repress strong emotions and prevent them from entering conscious awareness and perhaps overwhelming the person emotionally. Reich's was the first explanation of repression as a *physical* phenomenon.

This muscular armor leads to self–limiting behaviors, in that the person continues to behave only in a "characteristic" way, not in new or creative ways. According to Reich, behaving in a familiar pattern perpetuates neurotic or undesirable behavior.

Reich gradually moved away from orthodox analytic thought and stated that verbal remembering of childhood experiences must be accompanied by the original (but repressed) affect to be healing (1972, p. 24). This combination of cognitive memory with affect became his primary rule for therapy. By 1948, when he wrote the preface to the third edition of *Character Analysis,* Reich was working "bioenergetically" rather than analytically, using direct physical manipulation of the client's tight musculature to soften the armoring, thus dissolving emotional blocks and allowing the possibility of creative behavioral change (1972, p. xi). This process was totally unacceptable to the orthodox psychoanalytic community of the time. Gradually, however, his work gained a professional following, particularly in the United States.

Reich came to America during Hitler's rise to power in Europe and continued to develop his theories and techniques, including attempts at cancer treatment. He also continued to describe extensively the way that muscular armoring leads to personal and societal problems. Reich significantly influenced several followers in the psychotherapy field, two of whom were Alexander Lowen and Frederick ("Fritz") Perls.

Alexander Lowen, a New York–based therapist who is still practicing and teaching as of this writing, modified and elaborated many of Reich's ideas and turned them into a theoretical and practice–based approach first called "Bioenergetic Analysis," later "Bioenergetics" (Lowen, 1975). In *The Physical Dynamics of Character Structure* (1958), Lowen describes three purposes of Bioenergetic Therapy. First, the therapist analyzes both the client's psychological problems and their physical expression in the body. Second, the therapist uses direct touch for "systematic" physical manipulation of the musculature to release the chronic physical tension (or armor) of the patient. Third, the therapy work is done on both a physical and verbal level, thus involving the therapist more directly than in conventional therapy (p. ix). Lowen teaches clients to release their repressed emotions and resolve their personal conflicts by a combination of breathing techniques, stretching, "stress exercise," and direct hands–on manipulation of the client's muscular tissue by the psychotherapist.

Though thought controversial in psychoanalytic circles, Lowen's work has achieved considerable popularity. He was perhaps the first major theorist and therapist to support and discuss the use of physical interventions in psychotherapy *with* their accompanying professional, ethical, and therapeutic issues. He insisted that therapists using his methods must avoid any sexual touch in therapy. Lowen also advocated the use of therapeutic abreaction, that is, strong expression of past emotions within a therapy session. This work was designed to reduce and even change the client's emotionally limiting character armor. While many abuse survivors who have worked with bioenergetic–oriented therapists report finding the deep muscle work too invasive or too painful, Lowen's focus on abreactive work has proven to be a useful concept for many therapists in working with abuse survivors. Many professionals acknowledge the importance of Lowen's theoretical contributions, but have sought a less physically intrusive approach to bodywork.

Fritz Perls, an analyst originally influenced by Reich, came to America and originated the Gestalt therapy movement. Later influenced by both the humanistic movement and by Eastern philosophies, Perls placed considerable focus in therapy on the client's awareness of the body.

Perls stated, "Almost all persons in our society have lost the proprioception of large areas of their body. The loss was not accidental. It was, when it occurred, the only means of suppressing intolerable conflict. The issues which were then at stake, if now gradually reintroduced into awareness, can be worked through on a basis which actually resolves and puts an end to the conflict" (Perls, Hefferline, & Goodman, 1951, p. 85). Perls referred to massage as a technique whereby bodily awareness can be attained (p. 90), but did not follow up by suggesting massage as an adjunct to psychotherapy.

Perls always insisted that awareness alone was not sufficient for healing, but that working through ("finishing") the emotions was a crucial part of the therapeutic work. Perls regularly asked his clients to focus on breathing patterns and muscular holdings and to use the resulting awareness for change. Though Perls himself did not integrate touch with psychotherapy, some of his followers made regular use of touch in therapy (Marcus, 1979).

Perls formulated the theoretical and therapeutic concept of "unfinished business": people with unresolved traumas have stored or repressed emotions that have not been allowed expression and have had a negative impact on the person's body and behavior. When these repressed emotions are given appropriate expression in psychotherapy, clients are then able safely to feel the original emotions (often in an intense way), to integrate the emotional and cognitive learning into their lives, and then to feel "finished." This concept is often used in therapy with abuse survivors.

Just as Gestalt Therapy came to fruition during the humanistic movement of the 1970s, so also a variety of approaches to bodywork proliferated during that time. Perls, though not doing bodywork himself, encouraged Ida Rolf to continue her exploration of bodywork. Rolf (1989, first published in 1977) developed the bodywork technique that bears her name (Rolfing). Rolfing involves direct manipulation of the *fascia* (connective tissue encasing every muscle cell, fiber, nerve bundle, and organ in the body) in order to align the body correctly and enhance physical functioning. Though this manipulation often results in the release of repressed emotions, Rolf has neither incorporated psychotherapy into her work nor taught techniques for dealing with clients' emotions. Rolfers trained only in bodywork usually recommend that their clients go to a psychotherapist to process and integrate their erupting feelings. Rolfing seemed to embrace the "no pain, no gain" philosophy of the late 1970s and early 1980s, an approach abuse survivors may find too painful and intrusive.

Two other bodyworkers, Moshe Feldenkreis and F. Mathias Alexander, whose work became popular in the 1970s, have contributed to the development of the Psychophysical Model. Feldenkreis (1970, originally published in 1949) used physical manipulation and exercises in an attempt to correct posture and thus improve physical and mental health. His work is known for its gentle, noninvasive quality. Feldenkreis did not identify his work as psychotherapy, but rather as "movement education."

Starting in the 1890s, actor F. Mathias Alexander developed an approach to re-education of bodily awareness, called the Alexander Technique (Alexander, 1969; Jones, 1979). This technique focuses on the relationship of the head, neck, shoulders, and back, leading to kinesthetic awareness, a greater sense of relaxation, and a decrease in tension.

One of Alexander's students, Wilfred Barlow (1973), discussed the relevance of the Alexander Technique in working with neurotic disorders (p. 126). Barlow believed in the need for using the Alexander Technique in conjunction with psychotherapy for successful treatment outcomes. He referred to Alexander's approach as a "psychophysical orientation" (p. 140).

Both Feldenkreis' and Alexander's approaches work on restructuring the body's habitual postures with very subtle procedures focusing on awareness rather than deep manipulation of body tissues. While many clients report finding these approaches relaxing and soothing, others find that the process is too subtle and requires a level of bodily awareness that may be initially difficult for some abuse survivors to attain. Again, these techniques are not considered psychotherapy and are not designed for recalling or processing traumatic memories. Their concept of "movement education," however, is an important aspect of the Psychophysical Model in helping clients reclaim their full bodily awareness.

During the 1970s, many bodywork approaches centered on "reading" the body. Reading the body involves observing structural and postural function and dysfunction, locating physical and/or emotional holding patterns, and relating these observations to personality types. Kurtz and Prestera (1976), Dychtwald (1986, first published in 1977), and Keleman (1979) all used bodywork therapeutically with the conscious intention of discovering and releasing holding patterns. They contributed to the establishment of the concept of "bodymind" in the humanistic movement. Their work in turn was based in part on the theories of Wilhelm Reich.

In the 1980s, the emerging "bodymind" tradition continued with the contributions of Heckler (1984), Heller (Heller & Henkin, 1986), Juhan (1987), Rosenberg (Rosenberg, Rand, & Asay, 1989), and Kurtz (1990). All of these practitioners made varying and important contributions to the growing field of studying the relationship between the body and emotions and treating dysfunctional effects.

Two currently active psychotherapists who incorporate bodywork into their psychotherapeutic practice are Smith (1985) and Kepner (1987). In contrast to the team approach of the Psychophysical Model, these two therapists use a single–therapist approach to treatment, requiring the therapist both to touch the client and to simultaneously process the emerging psychotherapeutic issues.

This brief review of the work of various theorists, psychotherapists, and bodyworkers is by no means comprehensive, focusing primarily on practitioners who have influenced our work and the development of our model. While we have learned from them, there are also significant areas of difference between our understanding of bodywork and their theory and practice. The two most relevant differences involve "bodyreading" and the single–therapist approach to bodywork and psychotherapy.

We believe that "bodyreading" can be a somewhat limiting approach in bodymind therapies. A therapist who "reads" a client's body often imposes a doctrinaire framework that pre–establishes what emotions are stored in each particular area of the body. In such cases, the therapist is likely to find only what she or he is looking for. For example, a therapist looking for anger in the shoulder blades is likely to find and focus only on that, while missing the sadness or grief that may underlie the anger. In our experience, any emotion may be stored in any part of the body and different emotions may be stored in the same part of the body.

Single–therapist approaches may increase the *therapist's* ability to integrate his or her understanding of the client's emotional and physical issues. However, we believe that the use of *two* professionals, a bodyworker and a psychotherapist, best ensures the safety of the client and offers the highest level of skilled interventions in the process.

Why Bodywork Works

What all of these theorist–practitioners recognized to some degree is that, while verbal psychotherapy reaches some levels of cognitive and emotional memory, bodywork can provide access for the client and the therapist to deeper, less conscious memories and feelings while increasing the client's sense of self–awareness.

Smith (1985) has described the following pattern in psychotherapy: the client is encouraged to talk, leading to memories that may evoke cognitively based feelings. On the other hand, Smith suggests, when bodywork is used with psychotherapy, *feelings* (i.e., sensations *in the body*) are accessed directly. The evoked feelings then lead to increased memories from any or all of the senses (touch, taste, smell, hearing, sight) and can be relived or re–experienced within a safe context (p. 45). These *felt* memories are qualitatively different from cognitive memory. Smith's concept, with exceptions, generally fits our clinical experiences. His model reflects how we see the difference between traditional verbal psychotherapy and bodywork combined with psychotherapy.

The type of bodywork we use in the Psychophysical Model is what massage therapists often call "emotional release work," although "emotional facilitation" is perhaps a better term. Emotional trauma has a physical impact;

physical trauma carries an emotional impact. The two are bound together. The traumatic impact may show up as a pattern of chronic muscular tension (the armoring referred to earlier), postural distortion, limited range of motion, or a somatic–visceral response.[1] One effect of trauma is to limit movement, or limit people's ability to participate actively in choosing their own lives. By working with these limitations, discovering emotional blocks, and processing feelings and memories, clients can free their bodies and reclaim their lives.

A physical trauma such as sexual abuse is a specific event that affects the person's neuromuscular system and carries powerful emotions along with it. Any successful therapy for abuse survivors needs to address not only the emotion directly associated with what was done *during* the abuse but also the feelings *before* the abuse (anticipation, terror), and *after* it (anger, shame, guilt, fear). These emotions are assimilated inside the person, inside the musculature, as a way of managing or containing what would otherwise be too overwhelming or devastating. In addition, the body becomes conditioned against future similar occurrences: when "emotion A" is felt, it triggers an alarm ("Uh–oh!") that overwhelming "emotion B" might follow. The body and mind together then enact some kind of escape or avoidance routine that may become nearly automatic and may require a large expenditure of time and physical or emotional resources.

For example, perhaps a young boy was abused after practice by his coach who was wearing a blue windbreaker. The boy might then develop an unconscious anxiety or fear toward (and later an avoidance of) anyone dressed in a blue windbreaker, in order to protect himself from the fear he originally felt toward the coach who abused him. Later in life, even if he has not become amnesic about his abuse, he may find himself avoiding situations that might trigger a variety of confusing emotional reactions that result in anxiety, and yet not rationally know why. For example, he may avoid baseball games, or athletic events in general, expending energy and time to protect himself from feeling confused, anxious, or fearful, all because of the man in the blue windbreaker who abused him after practice.

Abuse survivors, like most people, commonly experience strong emotional responses to certain stimuli. This response has set up an intricate system of protection and defense for the abuse survivor, but at an out–of–awareness, or unconscious, level. The survivor may spend a great deal of energy and time avoiding the anxiety caused by seeing people in blue windbreakers, or picnics, or camp counselors, or locker rooms, or whatever it might be. Though their fear or discomfort seems irrational, it makes perfect sense when the root connection to traumatic stimuli is tapped. Working with the body is a powerful means of side-stepping the conscious mind and gathering information directly from the unconscious fund of knowledge.

---

[1] Somatic–visceral response occurs when pain is referred from muscle tissue to a visceral organ (stomach, spleen, liver, kidneys, intestines). Sometimes the pain is referred to muscles *from* these organs. For example, survivors often report feeling nauseous when working on other parts of the body.

3

Embodying Healing:
The Psychophysical Model

The Psychophysical Model is a team approach, offering collaboration between two therapists: a psychotherapist trained and skilled in helping clients integrate their emotional and cognitive insights in therapy; and a bodyworker trained and skilled in helping clients to increase their physical self–awareness and to gain access to emotions and memories through their bodies.

Among the many advantages to a team approach, two are of primary importance for the healing process. First, in working on issues of childhood sexual abuse, the client has access to twice the professional support and resources; and, second, an appropriate and nurturing structure offers a model for adult interactions with respect to boundaries. For the professionals involved, the team approach offers a built–in colleague/consultant to help when transference or countertransference issues arise. In this chapter, we present the Psychophysical Model and its goals, describe how it works, and discuss each therapist's role.

While many therapists are becoming increasingly interested in combining touch with psychotherapy, some are reluctant to use any ethical, appropriate touch in therapy for theoretical reasons or for fear that client misinterpretation of touch may result in lawsuits. In the Psychophysical Model, each therapist operates within the professional, legal, and ethical parameters of her or his profession. Although psychotherapists may ethically and appropriately touch a client with the client's permission, collaboration with a certified or licensed massage therapist who is professionally and societally sanctioned to touch a client therapeutically can help lessen a psychotherapist's ethical and legal concerns.

Similarly, any massage therapist naturally and appropriately makes verbal responses to a client's emerging emotions. In the Psychophysical Model, the massage therapist is free to concentrate primarily on the physical work, since a psychotherapist is available to help the client process and integrate emotions. At a time when it is becoming increasingly difficult for many professionals in mental health fields to feel comfortable using touch in psychotherapy, and given that any responsible psychotherapist or bodyworker wants to work within appropriate ethical and legal parameters, it makes sense to have someone who is certified or licensed to touch working therapeutically with abuse survivors.

A distinction must be made between the work of the psychotherapist and the bodyworker. Massage therapists generally respond with caring and supportive verbal comments to a client in distress and may ask general questions about feelings. For example, a massage therapist might ask, "What are you feeling right now? Can you describe the physical sensations you are aware of? Is there an emotion connected to this sensation? Does this feeling seem familiar?" In the Psychophysical Model, bodyworkers ask these types of questions to help the client clarify and identify their experiences and to gather information that may be valuable (and possibly unavailable) in the client's psychotherapy session. These questions should be both direct and general in order not to lead the client. Such interactions are not considered psychotherapy, and therefore are not outside the massage therapist's area of competence. A massage therapist is concerned with probing the neuromuscular effects of abuse, some of which may reveal memories and emotions. A psychotherapist is concerned with probing into the structure of the client's personality and helping the client integrate his or her complex emotional and cognitive expressions. In the Psychophysical Model, both the psychotherapist and the bodyworker work with the client's emotions, but at different levels and with different focuses.

The word *emotion* comes from the Latin word *emotio,* meaning a "moving away." All emotion is expressed through the musculature. Emotions and feelings are not frozen, crystallized experiences, they are movements. Most people can easily identify the outward muscular movements sometimes used to express anger or rage. These emotions, like sadness, fear, and others, may also be expressed by *inward* muscular movement, contraction, a sense of retreating inward. Regardless of whether the movement is outward (pacing, screaming, crying, laughing, dancing) or inward (flushing, tightening of throat, rising blood pressure), emotions are expressed through muscle movement.

Encouraging clients to fully embody their emotions is one goal of the Psychophysical Model. Healthy embodiment of feelings means being congruent: matching internal emotional feelings with external and internal physical behaviors. The experience of embodiment in bodywork can lead survivors to direct and honest expression of emotion, perhaps for the first time since the onset of the abuse. Clinicians often define congruence between internal experience and external behaviors as a major component of healthy personality.

The Psychophysical Model teaches the client how to differentiate between old, remembered pain, and present–day pain. For example, Joan, a female client in her mid–40's, accompanied a female friend to a restaurant for dinner. While waiting in the lounge area for their table, Joan and her friend were obviously enjoying themselves, laughing and talking animatedly. A waitress presented a round of drinks from a man at the bar with the message, "It's nice to see two attractive ladies out enjoying themselves. I admire your style."

Although both Joan and her friend were cognitively clear that the man was not making a sexual approach, the compliment threw Joan into an emotional tailspin, ruining the evening for her. Joan felt unsafe because she had been noticed and admired by a man. She cut dinner short and rushed home where she could feel safer. For the next week, Joan isolated herself and went on an eating binge. The current event (the man's compliment) had triggered emotions connected with childhood sexual abuse by a male, and Joan tried to cope with the pain using self–destructive behaviors.

Joan's psychotherapist saw this incident as one indication that Joan could benefit from bodywork. She felt shame and self–blame over her eating binge, feared that being touched in any way (even a friendly pat on the shoulder) would be sexual, and was generally not well associated with her body. In response to being touched on her hand or arm, Joan felt only panic over her whole body, not the physical sensation of tactile pressure in one location.

Bodywork and psychotherapy helped her discriminate the physical sensation of touch from the past emotions she had always associated with it. She learned to associate physical sensations to the parts of the body where they were objectively occurring. Joan's bodywork helped her experience touch as safe, nonsexual, and in a specific, limited location. In psychotherapy, she made the parallel realization that social situations which previously produced overwhelming anxiety (because of their potential threat of being sexualized like the abuse in her past) could be nonsexual, have nothing to do with past abuse, and be located in present–day, adult reality.

In the Psychophysical Model, by helping a client attend to current physical sensation, she or he learns to distinguish between today's emotion that needs to be expressed and released, and the memory of old emotions that hold the client back. The client comes to have an active choice of feeling and expression and need not feel overwhelmed with emotions.

Another goal of the therapeutic use of touch in our model is the recall of repressed or amnesic memories, by eliciting "muscle memory." Emotional as well as physical trauma is stored in the body. Although the traumatic episode may not be remembered consciously, the memories remain because of trauma–induced changes at the cellular level. The stored memories are available for retrieval and processing at an appropriate time. This concept of "muscle memory" is a foundation of the Psychophysical Model. Most bodyworkers are aware of the concept and have experiential evidence of muscle memory through their work.[1]

When we use touch to facilitate retrieval of amnesic memories, our purpose is to reframe the client's sense of self in relation to the abuse, not simply to re–enact the abusive episode(s). In facilitating recall, we first identify in psychotherapy sessions where the client's defenses are and discuss what function they serve. Part of the therapeutic process is to help the client determine whether these defenses are still relevant and effective in his or her present–day situation. One of our highest priorities is to respect where the client is emotionally and physically. We honor the function the client's defenses served in

---

[1] Promising work is being done on the psychobiology of emotions (Pert, 1986; Pert, Ruff, Weber, & Herkenham, 1985). Two books discussing these issues are *Mind, Brain, Body* (Reiser, 1984) and *Memory in Mind and Brain* (Reiser, 1990).

allowing the wounded child to survive to this point in time. No responsible therapist would remove a client's defenses and leave the client vulnerable.

The Psychotherapist's Role in the Psychophysical Model

Working with adult survivors of childhood sexual abuse requires the psychotherapist to have a broad and indepth knowledge of personality development; the ability to recognize, diagnose, and treat any psychopathology present; and the ability to help guide the client through abreactive expression and into appropriate integration and healing of emotions and memories. In addition, the therapist must be able to handle himself or herself appropriately and successfully in relation to the powerful emotions that may arise for the client in such work. This kind of therapy requires a therapist with a deep psychotherapeutic understanding of trauma and its many effects. Such therapy should be done only by a person who has prior training and supervision in working with adult clients, as well as an understanding of the dynamics involved in work with adult survivors of sexual abuse. The psychotherapist must also be able to accept and support the client's strong expression of painful emotions; working with abuse survivors is not for the faint of heart.

In the Psychophysical Model, the psychotherapist is the primary therapist and oversees the entire work with the client. When bodywork has not already been brought up by the client, the psychotherapist assesses when to introduce the concept of bodywork into the treatment program and with the client selects an appropriate body therapist for this important work.

The psychotherapist is responsible for screening and recommending bodyworkers. We recommend that a psychotherapist refer a client to a massage therapist for work with sexual abuse issues only after the therapist has first received bodywork from that massage therapist. Touch is a personal experience, and the psychotherapist must be clear for herself or himself about the bodyworker's approach, boundary issues, and general sensitivity toward clients. First-hand experience of the massage therapist's work allows the psychotherapist to explain the bodywork component in concrete detail to the client in discussions about adding bodywork to the therapeutic process.[2]

The psychotherapist is also responsible for determining whether and when bodywork is appropriate and helpful for the client by assessing the client's ego strength and level of dissociation (see McCann & Pearlman, 1990, pp. 126–130 for an excellent discussion of such an assessment). The client, of course, is free to accept or reject any recommendation for the concurrent use of bodywork in therapy.

---

[2] Some survivors seek bodywork on their own to help them move in their psychotherapy. As previously mentioned, Appendix B is designed to help clients who wish to seek bodywork outside the intentional collaborative structure presented here as the Psychophysical Model. See Appendix F for guidelines for psychotherapists on choosing a bodyworker.

Finally, the psychotherapist determines whether the client shows the presence of or potential for any psychotic processes. Bodywork may trigger a psychotic experience in an unprepared prepsychotic or Borderline client. Allowing this to happen would be harmful both to the client and to the body-worker, who may be unprepared to deal with such an occurrence. The psychotherapist must carefully screen and prepare the client for bodywork to avoid such problems.

Some Indications of the Client's Readiness for Bodywork

1. The client has an established and positive therapeutic relationship with the psychotherapist.
2. The client demonstrates an openness to being touched in a therapeutic manner.
3. The client reports dreams with traumatic physical content.
4. The client reports an increased experience and/or awareness of bodily discomfort or pain without a known physiological cause.
5. The client feels "stuck" in the verbal therapy process, yet knows there is more work to be done and wants a new perspective for the therapy.
6. The client has expressed a clear commitment to identify, work on, and resolve "unfinished business" about abuse.
7. A personal support system outside of therapy is available to assist the client when painful memories and strong emotions emerge within and between the therapy sessions.

These indications are guidelines that each psychotherapist can use as a basis for assessing whether a client can use the power of bodywork and still be safe. As always, client safety is of primary importance.

When the psychotherapist establishes that a client can benefit from bodywork, they discuss the concept in a therapy session, and the client then decides whether to explore the option. To reduce the client's anxiety and address concerns about bodywork, the client receives a handout (see Appendix C) on what to expect in a bodywork session as a basis for discussion.

The psychotherapist also guides and supports the bodyworker in understanding the emotional reactions of the client and in responding appropriately to them. For example, bodyworkers may not be familiar with the concepts of transference, countertransference, and projection (discussed in Chapter 7). The psychotherapist must help the bodyworker understand these concepts to increase therapeutic effectiveness and decrease his or her potential to be distracted by personal reactions.

Once bodywork commences, clients often come into psychotherapy with rave reviews of the massage therapist. One pitfall the psychotherapist can avoid is jealousy of the client's high regard for the bodyworker. The experience of safe, caring, nurturing touch often fills a need that many survivors don't know they have until it is met for the first time. Jealousy in this circumstance is inappropriate, unprofessional, and indicates that the psychotherapist may have countertransference issues with this client. Both the psychotherapist and the bodyworker must remember they are a team working with and for the client; both must be aware that their own egos may allow client reactions to divide them or create an inappropriate and ineffective sense of competition.

Regardless of the psychotherapist's experience in other treatment areas, professional supervision is highly recommended for psychotherapists who are inexperienced in working with abuse survivors. For psychotherapists with more experience in treating sexual abuse survivors, contracting for case consultation on an as–needed basis and/or peer supervision are suggested. While the Psychophysical Model provides a measure of built–in peer supervision/consultation, the more a psychotherapist and a massage therapist work together, the more likely it is that they will unconsciously develop the same blind spots. Contracting for supervision does not call into question the competence of the therapist, but recommends her or him as being willing to do extra work for the safety and benefit of all concerned.

The Bodyworker's Role in the Psychophysical Model

The bodyworker's primary role is to provide safe, nurturing, therapeutic touch in order to help the client gain increased body awareness, ease, and comfort. The bodyworker's therapeutic touching grounds the healing experience in the body for the client and makes it real. Other goals, such as recapturing memories and accessing emotions, are worked out by the client, the psychotherapist, and the bodyworker in the introductory nontouch session.

The bodyworker serves as a witness for the client as the client relives some of the painful memories of the past. By verifying the reality of the emotion for the client and providing an environment free of shame or guilt, the bodyworker helps to reframe the original trauma into memories and emotions that can serve as the basis for healing in the present.

The bodyworker makes significant contributions to the wellbeing of the client and to the therapeutic process. Bodywork helps a client renew his or her awareness of the physical experiences of the body. As bodywork continues to enhance bodily awareness, most clients learn how to describe their experiences of physical and emotional sensations. The connection between bodily process and cognitive understanding enhances the client's sense of self.

Bodywork also assists in reducing dissociation by helping the client become re–associated with bodily and emotional experiences and reclaim forgotten or denied parts of the self and of life. This re–association leads to greater integration of *experience* with the *self,* and thus to more complete healing.

Clients may come into therapy and eventually into the Psychophysical Model through bodywork. *Outside* the context of collaborative therapy, bodyworkers may see clients who express deep and painful emotions during massage sessions and then continue to have strong emotional reactions in bodywork sessions. When these clients are not in ongoing personal psychotherapy, the bodyworker should make an appropriate referral for psychotherapy. The bodyworker is not a psychotherapist, and having an outlet to express emotions in bodywork is different from therapeutically resolving emotional issues. It is part of the bodyworker's role to make this difference clear to the client.

When clients have strong emotional experiences during a bodywork session, the bodyworker needs to do more than touch. Appropriate verbal interventions are called for; supportive, nonjudgmental comments are always appropriate, without actually doing psychotherapy with clients. In effect, at such times the bodyworker's task is to help the client become stable and grounded enough to be safe until trained psychotherapeutic help is available. Massage therapists working with abuse survivors can benefit from supervision because of the intense emotions many survivors experience during bodywork sessions.

How Bodywork Contributes to Healing the Effects of Abuse

The bodyworker plays an integral part in the process of recalling repressed or amnesic memories. In a therapeutic massage session, clients often attain an altered state of consciousness. Breathing and brain–wave patterns change, and sometimes, while the client is in this relaxed state, images or memories float into his or her consciousness, somewhat as in a daydream or when under hypnosis. As the client verbally shares these images, they may become focused into greater clarity, leading the client to remember long-repressed traumatic experiences. Since some adult survivors of childhood abuse do not have conscious memory of their abuse, facilitation of memory recall is a major therapeutic contribution.

The concept that touch can help a person recall memories is familiar to most massage therapists. The bodyworker's touch must not and does not duplicate the original traumatic touch, nor does it need to. No *reputable* bodyworker (or psychotherapist) would ever touch or stimulate the genital area of a client. It is unethical, and anyone touching clients' genitals under the guise of therapy should be reported to the appropriate authority. For memory recall, this type of unethical touch is also unnecessary: the kinesthetic connection to the abuse was anchored in the body long before the abuser got to the genitals. The memory could be stored as a hand on the shoulder, or hip, or neck, or any place that may now be armored, "untouchable," or numb. This phenomenon of locating emotional responses and memories in the body may be related to the concept of "state–dependent memory."

In simple terms, "state–dependent memory" means that a traumatic memory is stored with emotion–linked chemicals in the body and the brain. When a childhood trauma occurs, the child is in a highly emotionally charged state, causing certain hormones known as neuropeptides or "messenger molecules" to be released into the body when the memory is being stored (Cousins, 1989; Pert, 1986; Pert et al., 1985). The bodyworker's touch may stimulate similar emotions that re–release these messenger molecules, thus allowing a previously repressed memory accompanying that feeling to arise in the client's conscious memory. Clients usually experience and express these memories, including images, sensory fragments, and emotions, in an intense emotional response. Their emotional reliving of the trauma in a therapeutic framework for purposes of integration and healing is what is meant by the term "abreaction."

There is no foolproof technique for working on a specific emotion or for recalling the related memories. Results come from how touch is experienced by the client and processed during the session using a variety of techniques. Emotions are not anatomically cataloged, either from person to person or within the same person from session to session. For example, we have found no basis for the belief that to elicit anger one should always work between the shoulder blades, or that work should always be done on the legs when dealing with support issues. We find styles based on such beliefs simplistic and limiting to therapists in how they interpret and respond to the client's affect. Working on the client's thigh may produce a particular emotion one week and a different emotion the next week. Emotional reactions also vary from one person to another. As Juhan (1987) comments, "The relationship between our experiences, our feelings, and our body chemistry is undoubtedly far more intricate than we can presently imagine" (p. 298).

Massage therapists often ask what specific theoretical approach to use in work with abuse survivors. Many styles and techniques can be effective. Most experienced bodyworkers have evolved an eclectic style that incorporates elements from various theoretical and practical schools. Any approach that respects the client's pain threshold and yet works deeply enough to access areas of chronic tension is appropriate. The bodyworker's awareness, attention, and compassion are the healing factors all techniques potentially share.

We find that Neuromuscular Therapy is a particularly useful approach in working with abuse survivors. Neuromuscular Therapy is a way of working in the deeper layers of the musculature while still remaining within the therapeutic comfort range of the client. The bodyworker uses enough pressure to be therapeutic (and it may often be uncomfortable) and yet not painful enough for the client to tighten up in resistance. It is effective in treating some of the physiobiological consequences of abuse, such as trigger points, limited range of motion, and postural distortion.[3]

Neuromuscular Therapy can be effective with somatic–visceral response, the referred sensation felt in the stomach, spleen, liver, kidneys, or intestines that is triggered from tension in the musculature (likewise pain in the muscles may be referred *from* a troubled organ). Like a psychotherapist, the Neuromuscular Therapist presses into the edge of the client's resistance, while not overpowering the client in any way or pushing him or her into pro-

---

[3] These *physiobiological effects* of sexual abuse are examples of how the sexual abuse is stored and expressed in the body. *Trigger points* are areas of high neurological activity that when stimulated can trigger sensations in some other part of the body. *Limited range of motion* can be seen when pain or tightness in the joints, ligaments, tendons, or muscles prevents a person's arms, legs, or torso from moving freely. *Postural distortion* shows in a client's unconscious, uneven way of standing, walking, or sitting.

tectively shutting down. This is a way of exploring dimensions of physical sensation and emotional feeling usually avoided by the client.

Bodyworkers and psychotherapists have different standards and different training. While the American Massage Therapy Association has developed a Code of Ethics (1992), when collaborating in work with a client, both therapists should adopt the more clearly defined standards of care from the field of psychotherapy, so that the rules for the treatment of a client are as clear as possible for all concerned. In using the Psychophysical Model of treatment for abuse survivors, massage therapists should familiarize themselves with the ethical standards of psychologists (American Psychological Association, 1992). These standards specifically require psychologists to work only within areas where they are trained, to maintain confidentiality, and to avoid any type of exploitive or harmful relationship with the client (see also Lerman & Porter, 1990).

How the Psychophysical Model Works

When the psychotherapist and the client agree that bodywork would be useful in the therapeutic process, the client receives a written information sheet on what to expect from bodywork (see Appendix C), along with a brief medical history form (see Appendix E). The client meets the bodyworker in the security and familiarity of the psychotherapist's office, where the client has established a feeling of safety and trust. Here the bodyworker benefits from the positive transferential umbrella of the therapeutic relationship already established by the client and psychotherapist.

This nontouch session begins with the psychotherapist and the client meeting alone for a few minutes, to see how the client is doing that day and to determine whether any urgent concern should take precedence over meeting the bodyworker. If not, the psychotherapist invites the bodyworker into the session with the client. The client is asked to share his or her therapeutic issues with the bodyworker to whatever degree the client is comfortable.[4]

The client usually asks the bodyworker questions (the nature of which may reveal new insight about the client). The purpose of this meeting is for the client to express his or her concerns regarding bodywork and the bodyworker and to receive honest, appropriate responses and reassurance as necessary in order to feel safe venturing into this new dimension in his or her treatment. At this meeting, the client also signs a release form giving permission for the massage therapist and psychotherapist to communicate regarding his or her therapy (see Appendix D).

A series of four appointments in the sequential mode (a bodywork session immediately followed by a psychotherapy session) are then scheduled over the course of the next month. These four sessions allow enough time for the client and the bodyworker to become familiar with each other; to address the

---

[4] The psychotherapist often gains insight by noting what the client shares and omits about his or her psychotherapeutic work, as well as from any new information the client may tell the bodyworker.

client's initial doubts, concerns, or fears; and to begin working on levels below the superficial muscle tissues of the body.

Rather than prescribing exact techniques that all practitioners *should* follow, we describe below how each of us works in the sequential mode. Practitioners can adapt this information to the styles they have developed.

The Sequential Mode — Massage Therapist / Patrick Connors

During the first bodywork session of the sequential mode, the client and I sit down and review treatment goals and approaches. I ask how the client is feeling and whether any concerns or issues have come up since we last talked. The idea is to spend some time getting reconnected before going into the touching portion of the session. I ask how the client is feeling in her or his body at the moment and where in the body the client chronically stores tension. I review the medical history form to look for any physical concerns that might contraindicate massage on a specific area of the body. Then we designate a starting place (for example, the client's back, shoulders or feet) for the bodywork.

I explain that physical sensations ranging from pleasure through discomfort and into pain are highly subjective and individualized. For example, light touch in a very sensitive area can be experienced as painful. In order to make this subjective phenomenon as objective as possible, I use a scale of sensations from "1" to "10." In this scale, numbers "1" through "5" represent a variety of sensations from pleasurable to neutral. The point where the client begins to feel discomfort is a "6," and "7" is clearly uncomfortable. An "8" is on the borderline between discomfort and pain where, if the client can take a deep breath and relax into the sensation, the experience of pain usually moves down the scale to discomfort.

On my sensation scale, "9" represents pain—too much pressure for *that* client at *that* spot at *that* time. I must reduce the pressure. The high end of intensity on the sensation scale is "10," a level that represents abusive work, resulting in possible damage to the physical tissues and definite damage to the client–therapist relationship. I never want to work in the "9" or "10" range. If a client specified that the pressure felt like a "9" during the massage, I would reduce my pressure immediately and ask the client about the feelings that were present.

For practitioners, the best area of therapeutic effectiveness to work in is the "6" and "7" range. The stimulus to the client's nervous system is sufficient to be physically therapeutic and to alter the normal patterning and sorting of information in the brain, providing some release of the "state–dependent" memory discussed earlier in this chapter. If I suddenly find myself working on what feels like an "8" to the client I stop movement and maintain the same amount of static pressure on that spot for about 10 seconds while encouraging the client to breathe more fully and to see what happens. After 10 seconds I ask my client what the current numerical reading is, and more likely than not, it has dropped to a "7" or even a "6." If it is still at "8," then I reduce my pressure so as not to risk damaging the therapeutic alliance I have established with the client. Work at that level no longer provides any physical benefit.

I explain to my clients, "At whatever point you begin to feel discomfort is where '6' begins. It is *your* body and *your* sensations we are tracking." When clients initially describe their physical sensations as "sore," "tight," or "achy," I ask them to add the numerical rating.

I talk with the client about "referred pain" and "trigger points." There may be hypercontracted (tight) dysfunctional tissues called trigger points in a muscle, so called because they "trigger" sensations in another part of the body. These referred sensations may be felt as pain, tingling, burning, itching, and so forth. These trigger points may even refer sensations to a visceral organ, producing feelings of nausea or an internal sensation of sharp, cutting pain. I ask the client to let me know when she or he feels these referred sensations because they can provide valuable information for reversing the physical consequences of abuse and for unlocking the secret to chronic muscular holding patterns.

I remind clients that they can work fully clothed or undress to whatever level they are comfortable with, and that they will be covered by a sheet. It is their choice. I say that in a minute I will be leaving the room to wash my hands while the client gets on the table. I suggest a starting position (face up or face down) on the table, and encourage the client to choose another position if the suggested one doesn't feel right. I show the client where she or he can hang up clothes. I explain that I will give the client a few minutes to get ready before I knock on the door and that I will wait to enter until I receive a "ready" response.

After I wash my hands, I knock on the door and wait for permission to enter. To begin, I usually encourage the client to establish a rhythmic breathing pattern where the duration of the inhalations and exhalations match. This simple shift in breathing can be enough to begin calming the body and slowing the brain's chatter.[5] The focus on breathing gives the conscious mind a task (as does the 1–10 sensation scale) so it is less likely to sabotage the unconscious process with negative, critical comments ("This is ridiculous, this will never work..."). Such comments are natural, a normal defense that guards against exploring the unknown. It is our job as therapists to push gently into this resistance to help the client see what is on the other side.

I might encourage the client to use this breathing pattern as a focusing tool or "homing device" if she or he starts to "space out" or "drift off" during the session. I mention that the client may see images or pictures in the mind's eye. Messages or memories may surface from the unconscious in many forms. Clients may smell a particular scent, experience a physical sensation, or hear a phrase spoken internally. If any of this sensory recall happens, I suggest

---

[5] This breathing pattern is suggested as a relaxation technique, not as a subtle hypnotic induction. Some clients do fall into a self–induced trance state, but that is not our intent.

that the client communicate it out loud without censoring or analyzing, avoiding the internal critic if possible. Speaking without censorship about whatever the client feels, sees, hears, or smells frees that thought or feeling so that the memory may unfold from deeper and deeper levels of the subconscious.

I physically work on the client's body with whatever style or technique intuitively feels right at the time, focusing on areas of chronic muscular tension or pain and following the flow of information coming from the client. When I get to a tender spot, a "6" or a "7," I move more slowly around (or even stop directly on) the most intense area of discomfort for about 10 seconds and ask the client what she or he is feeling. When the answer refers to physical sensations, I note the response and then ask what the client is feeling emotionally. Conversely, when the client's answer refers to emotional feelings, I note this response and then ask what she or he is feeling physically. Asking questions covering both physical sensations and emotional feelings helps me find out what the client is most connected to or disconnected from.

It is common for clients receiving massage to slip into a regressed state whether or not they are doing emotional work. I allow plenty of time at the end of the session to bring the client fully back to the present and into the functioning adult ego–state. I do a short piece of massage that feels good to the client and repeat it at the end of future sessions as a kinesthetic anchor, a signal that we have completed the touching portion of the session.

At this point I gently remove my hands and ask the client to rest for another minute or two on the table before slowly getting up. While I am still by the client's side I say, "I am leaving to wash my hands now. When you are dressed and ready, open the door—I will wait outside until you open the door." I also ask the client to pay attention to any feelings or images that arise after I leave the room so that we can talk about them when I come back. Then, as I am standing by the door to leave, I usually say, "These next few minutes are very important; please take your time." Then I remind the client once more that I will wait for her or him to open the door.

After washing my hands I look for the psychotherapist with whom my client is next scheduled, and we discuss for a minute what happened during the client's session with me to bring the psychotherapist up to date. In the sequential mode it is the responsibility of the bodyworker to retain the information recalled and verbalized by the client during the session, since the client may not remember some of it or what *is* remembered may be distorted by defense mechanisms.

When the client opens the door, I come back into my office, get a glass of water for each of us, and we sit down to talk for a few minutes. I ask the client what learnings or experiences she or he takes from today's session. Summarizing aloud tends to register the information in a solid, practical way in the client's cognitive awareness. If anything that seems important to me is omitted, I bring it up at this time and we discuss it. Was it important to me and not to the client? Did she or he just forget that part? Is that part something she or he is likely to deny or dissociate from? These questions will be fully processed in the psychotherapy session.

During this conversation I am making sure the client is in a strong adult ego–state, by looking to see that the eyes are clear and focused, and that she or he is associated to our conversation and to this point in time. If I have done my job well, the client's ego–state and level of association are rarely an issue; however, a client may appear associated and adult at the end of the massage and then may regress when left alone to dress. I make sure clients are fully present and grounded in the adult state before they leave my office. Drinking water, engaging memory to recall what happened for them in the session, confirming the next appointment time, and writing a check to pay for the session are all good grounding activities.

The Sequential Mode — Psychotherapist / Robert Timms

As Patrick indicated, while the client is dressing after the session I talk with the bodyworker to hear what happened in the bodywork session. There may have been memories that were partially (sometimes fully) recalled, anger about a certain person, or sadness about a particular memory or event. Sometimes the client has reported a dream she or he had since the last therapy session. Occasionally, I hear that the client was unusually quiet and unexpressive during the session.

After the bodywork session, the client comes into my office, where we discuss how and what she or he is feeling at that moment. We then set an agenda for the day, determined primarily by the client (though I may raise therapeutic issues from the week before). Although the agenda is usually based on what the client experienced in the just–concluded bodywork session, sometimes it includes an event that happened during the week and/or an ongoing therapy issue.

Whatever the session's content, I usually find the client more open, more responsive, and more fully present when she or he comes into my office directly from a bodywork session. The exception usually follows bodywork sessions where the client was quiet and nonexpressive. Often the client remembered something very painful and wanted to wait and share it in psychotherapy (perfectly appropriate); perhaps she or he had a dream about one of the two therapists and has been concerned about its meaning. Such dreams may vary in content, but are rarely sexual in nature.

One client, for example, reported a dream in which she as an adult had been in a public place, like a continuing education center, and was suddenly surrounded by several people who started stripping off her clothes. She was very frightened, when suddenly the bodyworker and I appeared in the dream, chased off the attackers, and covered her with a blanket.

Such positive transferential dreams are not uncommon during bodywork, and perhaps are best reframed to the client. I suggested to this client that her dream possibly acknowledged the support she was feeling from the therapists as she went through the painful process of peeling away old layers of outdated protection and appropriately yet painfully felt the residual childhood hurt underneath. Or, as T. Thomas (1990) has described it in his book of affirmations for abuse survivors, at this stage of therapy the client may feel like "all health is breaking loose." For growth to occur, at times the old pain and trauma must be re–experienced in a therapeutic way.

Often I find clients are better able to make cognitive connections in psychotherapy sessions that follow bodywork sessions. In most cases, the client's characteristic resistances are lowered and she or he is more available for therapeutic insight.

Occasionally, we do more affective and expressive work that may sometimes lead into an abreactive experience. Usually, however, abreactive sessions are planned in advance. When they spontaneously occur, it is my role to keep the client physically safe and to help her or him find a sense of personal and emotional safety as soon as possible. I do not touch the client during these experiences, unless it is necessary for me to use some physical restraint for the client's own safety and protection (an extremely rare occurrence, less than a dozen times in more than 20 years of practice), or unless he or she directly asks me to touch him or her. Just as any responsible massage therapist attends to the client's emotions and makes any needed verbal responses, so at times it is appropriate and necessary for the psychotherapist (with the client's permission) to touch the client in a supportive, grounding way.

After this type of expressive work, I help the client return to a fully present and adult ego–state, and we discuss, process, and integrate the emotional experience into the cognitive portion of the client's life. I doublecheck the client's appropriate adult level of functioning before she or he leaves my office. If the client has done strong abreactive work, we discuss the possibility that other reactions may surface later in the day or evening, and I encourage the client to call me if an emergency arises. After such a session, we usually make an agreement that we will speak briefly by phone the next day.

Sometimes clients recall more memories and experience strong emotions after the session. Unfortunately, some therapists have been taught to regard this process as "decompensation" leading to a possible psychotic break or suicide attempt; it is sometimes regarded as a mark of the therapist's failure or misjudgment. Abreaction or even post–traumatic stress flashbacks in survivors of childhood sexual abuse are not decompensation (for an interesting discussion of abreaction and decompensation, see Briere, 1989, pp. 132–135). None of my clients has had a reaction severe enough to require hospitalization after abreactive work. In my clinical experience, either clients needing hospitalization have been repressing too many strong old emotions, or the crisis leading to hospitalization was precipitated by a real external experience in current life unrelated to therapy events.

On the rare occasion that the client requests it, or when I think it would be a good idea, we schedule an extra appointment before our next (usually weekly) appointment. After the client leaves, if any significant information has been revealed that pertains to the bodyworker and that part of the therapy, I discuss it with the bodyworker.

After four sequential sessions, the two therapists and the client evaluate the client's progress, and may continue in the sequential mode for a longer time; or we may determine either that a combined session would now be more helpful, or that the bodywork will be discontinued.

Massage Therapist and Psychotherapist: The Combined Mode

In a combined session, both therapists meet with the client in the bodyworker's office. The three sit and discuss what the client is currently feeling and what issues she or he brings to that day's session. The two therapists leave the room as the client undresses (to whatever level feels comfortable), gets on the massage table under a sheet, and gives permission for the therapists to enter the room.

When the two therapists return, the psychotherapist takes a seat close to the client's head, so the client can see the psychotherapist and the psychotherapist can hear the client. The massage therapist begins to work on the client's body, paying special attention to areas of chronic pain or numbness, or areas specified in discussion at the start of the session. As emotions arise, the psychotherapist helps the client process them. The therapists are working with a client who is *experientially* remembering (reliving) a past trauma, not just *cognitively* remembering it.

The bodyworker follows much the same pattern as in the sequential mode, helping the client focus attention on breathing and bodily sensations. In response to the bodywork, a client may see images, hear thoughts, or recall memories. For example, in one combined session, the client reported seeing an image of a bookshelf. The psychotherapist responded with a gentle request for more information: "What do you see on or around the bookshelf?" The client saw that the bookcase was in a hallway leading into a room in the house where his family lived when he was young. Continued exploration of this visual image led him to recall his father beating him in that room and to his expressing strong feelings of anger and sadness.

The psychotherapist takes primary responsibility for the verbal processing of the client's experiences, just as the bodyworker's primary responsibility is to attend to the body. However, since we use a team approach, each therapist is open to giving and receiving suggestions during the combined session about possible areas to explore with the client. Both therapists attend to the passage of time, and either may signal the end of the session. The psychotherapist asks the client whether anything is unfinished in the session. When the massage work ends, the bodyworker usually asks the client to pay attention to any feelings or images that arise after the therapists leave the room, and requests that the client rest for another minute or two before slowly getting up from the table. The bodyworker and psychotherapist leave the room; the client rests, then dresses, and opens the office door when ready, as a signal for the therapists to return.

On returning to the room, the bodyworker offers the client a glass of water, and one of the therapists asks the client what insights and experiences occurred during the session. Again, by reviewing the session with the client, the therapists can fill in any memory gaps and correct distortions. In addition, having the client say out loud what happened helps her or him anchor the experience in present–day cognitive memory. When both therapists are assured the client is in an appropriate, fully functioning adult ego–state, the session ends. On the rare occasion that a client has difficulty returning to an adult ego–state, we make our "safe room" available for the client to rest in and ask the client to check in with one of us before he or she leaves.

We are often asked about the length and cost of combined sessions. Typically, a combined session lasts an hour, though the client may contract in advance for an extended session of up to four hours. Each of us charges his usual fee. Though this seems initially more expensive, we have found that the use of the Psychophysical Model greatly decreases the length of the overall therapeutic process, making it less expensive in the long term.

Special Concerns

While most survivors can handle the experience of bodywork and learn to differentiate between old, remembered trauma and current emotional experiences, some cannot. Persons who are psychotic and clients with certain personality disorders are unable to differentiate between reality and fantasy or between past and present. For example, clients with an *accurate* diagnosis of Borderline Personality Disorder (BPD)[6] should rarely be treated with bodywork. The professional psychological literature is clear that such clients may experience abreactive expressive work as current abuse. These clients may find it difficult to distinguish between what happened to them as children and what is happening today in therapy.

When a psychotherapist thinks bodywork would be useful for a client with BPD, he or she can promote a positive outcome by communicating clearly and directly to the bodyworker what precautions need to be taken for each individual client, and at what speed the bodyworker should proceed. Usually a combined session is indicated with borderline clients to minimize distortions, reduce transference problems, and help the client work through any emotions that arise.

In the Psychophysical Model of therapy, we want to avoid emotionally overstimulating clients, so that no one is flooded (overwhelmed) with affect. Clients overwhelmed with emotion usually shut down, rather than learning from and integrating experiences therapeutically.

---

[6] This diagnosis has often been inaccurately and indiscriminately applied to adult female survivors of child sexual abuse. While the presentation and issues are similar, the etiology (how the symptoms develop) and prognosis (possibility of recovery) differ markedly. For a discussion, see Briere (1989, pp. 35–39). A history of childhood sexual abuse, however, does not automatically exclude the possible presence of any personality disorder, including BPD (for a clear, basic text on BPD see Kreisman & Straus, 1989).

The therapist's job is to help the client safely get through the experience of remembering emotions. Working within the "therapeutic window of affect" (Cornell & Olio, 1991) involves finding an appropriate level of emotion for each client that is therapeutically useful; either too much or too little affect weakens the therapeutic experience. Too much affective stimulation leads to dissociation; too little affect may lead to intellectualizing or otherwise defensively avoiding the emotional experience. Good therapeutic comments can help the client appropriately increase or decrease the affective level.

After an emotion–laden session, the therapist is responsible for seeing that the client leaves the office well grounded in the adult ego–state. For example, a client may need to rest in the waiting room or in another safe area before driving a car or going to pick up children.

When an abreactive session is planned in advance (and in general they should be) the client may need to plan for time free from adult responsibilities after the session. The client needs a chance to assimilate what has been experienced and learned. Perhaps the client will want to call a friend to come over to talk, to hold the client, or to offer some other comforting support.

In summary, in the Psychophysical Model, information in the form of memories and/or emotions often results from the bodywork session. This new or clearer information is discussed by the psychotherapist and the client in the psychotherapy process. As these issues and emotions are worked through therapeutically and integrated into the person's current life experiences, the traumas of the past can recede into historical perspective and become less of a problem in the client's current life. For many clients the model provides the opportunity for much faster progress in recovering from childhood sexual abuse (see Appendix G for a summary of the benefits of the Psychophysical Model).

4

Touching the Dynamics of Abuse

We have already noted some reasons we think it is important for abuse survivors to do abreactive work in therapy. Remembering and reliving the trauma with the full emotion that was denied expression at the time, and with a full sense of present–day safety within the therapeutic setting, gives clients a new and healing perspective on the abuse and on themselves. In the long term, experiential therapy for survivors leads to greater comfort and satisfaction with life.

However, therapeutic abreactive experiences may feel uncomfortable and frightening for the survivor while they are occurring. Survivors may unconsciously use old protective patterns of coping to prevent past emotional pain from surfacing by avoiding abreactive work. Because coping and avoidance patterns need to be recognized and addressed by the survivor and both therapists, this chapter briefly explains their dynamics.

The 3–D Defense

The most frequently encountered coping mechanisms found in survivors are denial, distortion, and dissociation (the three D's). Distortion and some forms of dissociation can be viewed as forms of denial, as suggested below.

Repression is denial of fact ("Nothing happened"). Amnesia is a denial of memory ("Something may have happened, I don't remember"). Dissociation can be viewed as a denial of personal experience ("It happened, but not to me"); clients often express dissociation as "leaving the body." Distortions usually reflect any of three perspectives: a denial of impact ("It happened to me, but it doesn't affect me"); a denial of self–worth ("I'm bad because I was abused," or conversely, "I was abused because I'm bad"); or an inability to assign responsibility to the perpetrator ("It was my fault").

Denial

Repression and amnesia (both discussed earlier) are examples of a protective denial of awareness that frequently occurs when survivors have unconsciously banished any thought or memory of the abuse from their conscious minds. Repression and amnesia *defend* the survivor's consciousness from overwhelming memories of pain. Bodywork can play a significant role in dissolving these two types of denial.

Though many clients enter psychotherapy with some degree of denial about childhood abuse, by the time the bodyworker is invited into the therapeutic process the initial denial is usually either lowered or gone. It frequently reappears, however, as the client gains access to *new* memories of childhood abuse and/or new feelings via the body. The initial reluctance of many clients to believe that the abuse they are beginning to remember really happened is a manifestation of denial. In essence the client says, "Nothing happened to me," when she or he means, "I *wish* nothing had happened to me." Such denial is a usually temporary part of the normal memory retrieval and recovery process.

Amnesia, however, may often be present as the client starts bodywork, and is one reason for incorporating bodywork into the therapeutic process. Since bodywork can help the client recall repressed or amnesic memories, bodyworkers should be prepared for clients to express strong feelings when hidden memories suddenly return during bodywork sessions.

Distortion

Bodyworkers frequently encounter and have the opportunity to correct cognitive distortions for clients who have inaccurate perceptions of their own bodies. Survivors also may have inaccurate (usually minimized) perceptions about what was done to them in childhood. Distortions such as denial of impact are cognitively learned and culturally determined. Most adult survivors learned denial during childhood from society's pretense that sexual abuse did not exist. Clients may remember the event of the abuse, but deny that it was abusive. Clients who learned this kind of denial (especially males) describe the abuse using phrases such as, "He didn't really hurt me," or "She gave me an early start in learning about sex." Male survivors frequently assure therapists, "Sure, it happened, but I've put it all behind me. It wasn't that big a deal." If that were true, there would be no covert symptoms or other indications of unresolved abuse issues. Full resolution of the trauma becomes impossible until the impact of the abuse is no longer denied.

Distortions can result from early childhood experiences in a dysfunctional family. Child victims may create elaborate explanations in order to bring the abuser's otherwise inexplicable behavior into some kind of congruence. As previously noted, children who are sexually abused by a parent or other caretaker on whom they must depend for food, shelter, clothing, emotional nurturing, approval, and other necessities of life, live within an impossible double bind. This double bind (having to depend on the abuser for survival) produces and perpetuates distortions. Whatever distortions were necessary for victims to survive can become solidified and carried over as their adult reality. Adults who see life through these old beliefs tend to add many more distortions based on the earlier ones ("My father hurt me; my father is a man; all men want to hurt me"). Almost all of these distortions have a negative impact on the life and happiness of the survivor.

Cognitive distortions can be difficult to identify because they have become habitual trains of thought and are no longer a conscious part of the decision–making process. The survivor can begin becoming aware of his or her distortions by recalling family sayings or family "myths": "You were always your father's favorite," or "Your aunt was a saint to take you in and take such good care of you."

One goal for the adult survivor beginning treatment is to return the survivor's adult state to the time of the original wound and reinforce the child's original and accurate perceptions: "Yes, what he (she) did was wrong, bad, and icky"; "yes, you were right, it wasn't a game"; "yes, you were a victim, not an instigator, not a partner"; and most important, "what the abuser did to you was all the abuser's fault."

Distortions also occur in clients with personality disorders. These distortions are usually caused by intense anxiety in clients, preventing them from either hearing accurately what is being said or understanding it clearly and rationally. Although clients with personality disorders can be worked with using the Psychophysical Model, it is better in our opinion to delay bodywork with them until they are at a stage of their psychotherapy where they are able to make appropriate and healthy use of it.

Dissociation

Dissociation is present to some degree in almost everyone in the form of daydreaming, being on "automatic pilot" while driving, fantasizing about the "somewhere else" one would rather be than where one is (at the dentist's office, in a boring lecture, etc.). Another form of dissociation occurs when a person feels "outside the self," like an observer without emotional connection to the everyday events of the person's life. Survivors of severe traumas such as childhood sexual abuse may dissociate more frequently and to a greater degree.

People learn early in their psychological and physical development to *associate* external events in life with internal sensations and perceptions. As this happens, one becomes connected, or "associated," with life events. When a major trauma such as sexual abuse occurs, the child may automatically protect himself or herself by the unconscious use of dissociation: in effect, the mind and spirit of the child "go away" to a place of emotional safety, leaving the body behind to endure the abuse. Clients often report that they "drifted out the window" or "watched from the ceiling."

Although the experience of the abuse is stored in the body (muscle memory), the child minimizes from consciousness the extreme emotional and physical pain of abuse by this process of dissociation. The pattern of dissociation usually continues into adult life. During times of stress or pressure, the survivor may again have a dissociative experience and avoid psychological or physical pain by becoming numb or simply not present. While most adult survivors enter psychotherapy with some degree of dissociation, the addition of bodywork to treatment helps them recognize their dissociation and gently become associated or connected to their bodies.

In more severe dissociation, a person may develop personality fragments, each dealing with a particular stressful event or emotion. Some psychotherapists may mistake this situation for Multiple Personality Disorder
(MPD), though the *Diagnostic and Statistical Manual, Third Edition–Revised*
(American Psychiatric Association, 1987) defines this level of dissociation as a
"dissociative disorder, not otherwise specified" (p. 277).

True MPD occurs more often than previously thought (Putnam, 1989)
and is sometimes encountered in therapeutic work with survivors. In MPD, a
person develops two or more fully separate personalities (alters), each having a
developmental history and serving a (sometimes unapparent) protective function. Severe physical and/or sexual abuse, common in the etiology of MPD, is
one of several possible causes (Kluft, 1984). Contrary to popular media's
extreme images of MPD, most people would not necessarily be able to tell
whether a friend, relative, or acquaintance is a multiple. Working with an experienced psychotherapist, clients with MPD may get their alters to communicate
and become allies for them, and in some cases they may integrate some or all of
their personalities.[1]

While bodywork should not be initially used in treating clients with
MPD, it can be valuable during some of the abreactive and integrative phases of
therapy. The psychotherapist must ensure that all known alters have given permission for bodywork and that all known alters are introduced to the bodyworker. Bodyworkers must be aware that while it may appear they are working
on the same body, each alter may have a different pattern of muscular tension
or even a different somatic issue: one alter may have high blood pressure, while
another has arthritis (Bloch, 1991; Cawthra, 1992).

Ego–states[2]

In our work with adult survivors of sexual abuse, we find it useful to
conceptualize the client's internal personality organization into several
"ego–states." Various writers have different descriptions of such states: Eric
Berne (1961) writes of the parent, adult, and child ego–states; John Bradshaw
(1990) talks and writes about the inner child. In our practice, we refer to three
ego–states: a child ego–state (the child), an adult ego–state (the adult), and a
critical ego–state (the critic). We believe these ego–states exist in every adult
human being.

---

[1] Hocking and Company (1992) identify four potential levels of integration, any of which
is a valid choice for a multiple: 1) *remaining multiple;* 2) *cooperation,* where all alters communicate and work for the good of the host; 3) *joining,* where alters remain themselves but act in closer
concert to handle specific tasks or situations than is characterized by *cooperation;* and 4) *integration* of alters into a single personality (pp. 71–74).

[2] This discussion of child, adult, and critical ego–states applies to most people and does
not imply the presence of MPD.

The Child

The child ego–state is based on the actual child we were at about age five or so. This part of us thinks, feels, and reacts like a child, with a child's logic. For survivors of pre–adolescent sexual abuse, the child ego–state is usually the repository of the memories and emotions of the sexual abuse.

During either bodywork or verbal therapy, the client may regress to a point where the child ego–state is dominant. The therapist can recognize this regression by the client's changed vocal tone and/or language (shorter, simpler words), increased willingness to express pain, and use of child–like logic and reasoning. Although physically the bodyworker is still working on the same body, emotionally the client has shifted into the child ego–state. To continue to work effectively with the client, the bodyworker must also shift focus.

Children have more needs and fears than adults and are usually less hesitant to express them. Therapists need to be aware of the client's ego–state and be especially responsive to the appropriate needs of the child ego–state. At these times, it is helpful for the therapist to be even more gentle and more supportive of the client.

For example, when dealing with painful memories in therapy, the client may enter a child ego–state and call out for the therapist (or for the nonabusing, but nonprotective parent) by name. One helpful response is for the psychotherapist simply to say, "I'm here, what do you need?" and for the bodyworker to continue with gentle, supportive touch. The child may respond by thinking, "Thank goodness *some* adult is here."

Both therapists model behavior that shows the client's child and adult ego–states how to be present in a nurturing, caring, and protective way for a hurting child. In reassuring the client's child–self, the therapist needs to be careful not to criticize or invalidate in any way the emotions expressed ("You shouldn't be scared—you're safe now" versus "I hear that you're scared, it feels scary to you, and I'm right here with you").

Eventually the client learns to be a good parent for herself or himself. The use of two therapists offers a "good parent" model, in that the two professionals provide twice as much support and opportunity of healing for the client. While we don't do "reparenting" in the sense of doing for the client what she or he needs to learn to do personally, we do offer an example of good parenting in caring for the client's wellbeing through our modeling of acceptance, good boundaries, and other appropriate behaviors.

The Adult

The adult ego–state is the rational, information–processing part of us, and also has the responsibility for loving, caring for, and protecting the self and significant others. The adult often "disappears" when a person dissociates during times of painful emotion, leaving the client's child–self feeling helpless, confused, and abandoned. Therapy helps strengthen the adult, thereby helping the client become better at self–parenting.

The Critic

For most people, the critical ego–state comes into existence early in childhood and reflects internalized (introjected) criticisms of the child by parents and other adults. As this formation grows, it tends to become increasingly critical of the adult ego–state, and at times may attack the child ego–state as well. The original function of the critic may have been to protect the abused child by anticipating the negative demands and characterizations of abusive adults in the child's life. In the present, the adult must learn to protect the child and limit the negative activities of the critic.

Rather than trying to dissolve or destroy the critic, an appropriate goal of therapy is to turn the critic to positive use on behalf of the client. There is still need for protection in the world, and the critic can join forces with the adult, adding its resources and instinct for survival.

In abuse survivors, these three internal ego–states often engage in extremely negative and unhealthy communication. Often the adult does not want to deal with the child's severe pain. The adult usually wants to disconnect from the painful part of the self, and deny that the abuse actually happened to him or her in childhood ("That happened a long time ago, I was a different person then").

Not wanting to feel the emotional wounds of the trauma or deal with its consequences, the adult denies and dissociates. The child feels this denial and abandonment and appropriately distrusts the adult's willingness and ability to keep the child safe, or to prevent the child from getting into dangerous and scary situations again. When its needs are denied, the child may sabotage the adult by procrastinating, overeating, acting out inappropriately, drinking, using drugs, and/or becoming depressed.

The critic then joins the sabotage and widens the communication gap by emphasizing to the child how the adult–self is inattentive and unavailable, just as the parents were. Or the critic may take the side of the adult to help squelch the child's feelings and memories. These feelings and memories are then turned inward, often leading to somatic stress symptoms.

One of our therapeutic goals is to help the client develop more respectful communications between the child and the adult ego–states. The critic can be enlisted as an ally of the therapist and taught to incorporate new, healthy introjects supporting the collaboration of the adult and child ego–states in protective, nurturing interactions. When therapy is successful, the critic, the adult, and the child ego–states may become fully integrated, allowing the client to move beyond victim and survivor identities, into fully thriving self–actualized personhood.

5

Embodiment:
The Benefits of Touch in Therapy

At least two conditions are necessary for clients to transform old patterns of passivity: increased self–awareness and a desire to change. Self–awareness requires being in the present, living in or feeling one's own body, as opposed to living only in one's head. This state of being fully present physically and mentally is "embodiment." When a person is present, she or he is tuned in to the situation as it is happening now, without an overlay of emotions based in old memories. The embodied person can respond more appropriately in the moment, rather than repeating a negative script from dozens or hundreds of times before. The client can become an active participant, with options and possibilities that seemed nonexistent before.

In the Psychophysical Model, touch is a *means to an end,* facilitating the client's awareness of self. As a means to an end, touch can demonstrate to clients who may be unaware of it the existence of their own physical tension. Often clients do not experience themselves as tense until the bodyworker touches a particular spot ("I didn't know I was tight there," or " I didn't know I was sore"). Abuse survivors are often unaware of their bodily sensations. Once the existence of tension is recognized through massage, the bodyworker can help clients release it, decreasing survivors' pain and increasing their comfort. This experience can be profound within a single one–hour bodywork session.

Clients typically experience a whole range of changes from denial and/or tension to awareness, presence, and ease, so that they come to see the possibility of a whole new way of being in their bodies. Embodiment offers the possibility of a life free of the pain and shame survivors may have connected to their bodies in the past, so that living in their bodies in the present can feel comfortable, even pleasurable. This sense of reclaiming the body is empowering for the client and a necessary step in recovering from childhood abuse. When embodiment is experienced as healing, there is hope. As Yalom (1985) has pointed out, a primary purpose of any therapy is awakening and maintaining hope in the client.

Touch can also be *an end in itself.* Touching just for the sake of touching is a basic human need, called "skin hunger." All human beings have a need to give and receive safe, nurturing, appropriate touch. In working physically with abuse survivors, the bodyworker may discover that some clients are not touched except during their massage sessions. Many abuse survivors experience a touch deficit, and some survivors fear touch so much that they arrange their lives to avoid it. Ashley Montague (1971), in his book *Touching,* posits that we all have a need to touch and to be touched. Research now being done with massage on premature infants at the University of Miami (Field, 1991), has shown that premature infants receiving massage exhibit increased rates of physical growth and progress, demonstrating how important touch is to the human system. We all have a need to receive information from the outside world to help define our internal experiences.

Therapeutic touch offers clients a new experience, giving them new information about their bodies and their lives. It moves awareness out of their "heads," or intellects, and into their bodies. Different sensations are available in different areas of the body. It is important for clients to learn their areas of comfort and discomfort. As clients become aware of physical sensations in different areas of their bodies and at different times and settings in their lives, they gain new information that allows and even encourages new choices.

In the Psychophysical Model we use touch to bridge the gap between physiological awareness and verbal expression. Touch is a uniquely effective tool in accessing preverbal trauma when the client was simply too young to remember cognitively, but had feelings, images, and sensations that can be stimulated and recalled through touch and expressed in sounds rather than words.

The Psychophysical Model allows for safe and appropriate expression of the client's repressed strong emotions (through abreactive work) that are then worked through, resolved, and integrated in psychotherapy. These feelings may include grief, anger, and fear.

Using bodywork rather than hypnosis to recall childhood events or traumas allows the client to be more in charge of what is recalled, and to have ready access to the memory. Although hypnosis is useful in diagnostic work and in psychotherapy with severely dissociated clients, we prefer that clients recall the memory of their trauma when they are ready. When clients come to their memories through bodywork, they know it is based on physiological responses, and not on any perceived hypnotic or post–hypnotic suggestion by the therapist.

Touch can help define the body's boundaries. Survivors really need to know *where* they are, *who* they are, and *how* they are. If they often approach life from the child's perspective, they may not realize how big, strong, and powerful they actually are in present–day reality. Resistance exercises, a type of bodywork in which clients push against the bodyworker's hands or shoulders, for example, help ground clients' realizations of physical strength in present–day time. Survivors may discover themselves to be much stronger and more capable than they feel emotionally.

Many survivors, no matter how competent and functional they are in some areas of their lives, often present themselves as passive. They may perceive themselves as undeserving and unworthy (the "damaged goods" syndrome). This perception can lead survivors to a sense of passivity, thinking they deserved nothing better. With few significant assertive role models (or none), some survivors may be passive in adulthood because resistance in childhood was futile: since as children they fought as hard as they could against the abuse and it did no good, they may still think there is no point in standing up for themselves today.

All of our clients who are adult survivors of childhood sexual abuse have been abused more than once or by more than one person. This revictimization often occurs when a survivor engages in an adult activity that begins as mutual behavior, then shifts and becomes abusive. When survivors believe their own needs are not worth meeting, they tend to accept what is left after the needs of others have been met. The perception of unworthiness fosters revictimization and prevents clients from standing up for themselves. As clients become embodied in the present through bodywork and therapy, most come to see themselves as normal, not damaged or crazy. They engage life more actively and stand up for themselves as human beings worthy of being treated well by others.

As clients engage life more actively, they are more likely to take appropriate responsibility for their own behavior and its consequences, in contrast to feeling like a victim. When they first enter therapy, abuse survivors may blame other people or circumstances when things go wrong, a kind of distorted thinking that reinforces their victim identity. It is as if survivors learned from society's denial that they were "wrong" about the abuse happening, "wrong" about how bad it felt, and "wrong" about who was at fault; they have no space to be "wrong" about anything else.

Taking *responsibility*, however, is not self–*blame*. Acknowledging responsibility for how one lives is claiming personal power in life; seeing responsibility as a burden maintains a victim perspective. Personal power lies in recognizing true responsibility and accountability. Both tools are necessary in making the shift from a passive to an active lifestyle.

Just as pain brings *dis*sociation, pleasure brings *a*ssociation. Since many abuse survivors fear the pain involved in new, risk–taking experiences, they may adopt a passive lifestyle. Because fear of pain is stronger than pursuit of pleasure, they may be locked into this passivity. As their perceptions change with therapy, the ability to have pleasure without fear increases. As emotional and physical pain decreases, and pleasure in life increases, the client has an added incentive to be fully embodied.

Another benefit of bodywork is improved body image and decreased shame. By being touched in a healthy, nonjudgmental, accepting manner during bodywork, the client grows increasingly aware that she or he is neither shameful nor repulsive and is a normal, worthwhile individual. When the bodyworker does not pull away physically or emotionally during the client's sharing of an intense emotional response, the client's sense of shame decreases, and her or his sense of acceptance increases.

Working within the Psychophysical Model, a client may for the first time in adult life have a *realistic view of her or his own body*. Equally important, the survivor may start to see her or his body as others see it: not as a monument to a horrible tragedy, but simply as a body.

In receiving therapeutic bodywork, a client experiences being touched and contacted by a person who does not have critical judgments about the client's body. As the bodyworker responds to a client with acceptance and respect, the client can take in these new data. To feel and believe, "I can be touched without being hurt," and/or "I'm not like the person who abused me: I can touch others responsibly, safely, and without hurting them," are major new insights that can change the client's self–image.

As survivors focus their awareness of the body in a healthy way, they can begin to look at themselves differently. In accepting themselves as they are, they may then elect to change as they no longer consciously or unconsciously feel a need to punish themselves through their bodies. As one of our clients said, after therapy, *"I am no longer a prisoner in my body."*

When the body is a more comfortable place to be, a survivor is more likely to be embodied and aware of his or her sensations. This new sense of being present in the body encourages a survivor to be more fully present in her or his life, enhancing the survivor's enjoyment, and increasing the survivor's zest for life. Survivors may change their clothing styles, dressing in brighter, more cheerful colors; they may style their hair differently. Accepting the body as the self, rather than as the enemy, suddenly opens up a new realm of possibilities for new sensations, new expressions, and new emotional and physical experiences to be savored. Clients may sign up for a dance class, try a new sport, or find other ways to enjoy rather than deny their bodies.

By incorporating bodywork into the healing process through the Psychophysical Model, clients get an opportunity to reframe their cognitive perceptions of themselves both in relationship to the abuse and in their whole concept of touch. Rather than feeling aggressive, abusive, and harmful, touch is experienced as healing and nurturing. Clients have the experience of deciding if and when, by whom, and how to be touched, and of having those boundaries respected.

6

Working in the Psychophysical Model: "Joan" and "Paul"

This chapter combines client accounts and case notes of two clients from our practice. Both "Joan" and "Paul" (not their real names) have written their own narratives. We have added our comments to elaborate on some aspects of their therapeutic experiences. In our practice, case notes are kept by the psychotherapist: unless otherwise noted, the commentary below is by psychotherapist Robert Timms.

"Joan"

When a psychotherapist specializes in working with adult survivors of sexual abuse, clients are likely to disclose their secret (often for the first time) during the initial session, as Joan did.

> I was trapped in my own body. Trapped as surely as if incarcerated in a cell, secured by the rusty lock of time with the secrets of my life swallowing the key.
>
> I am a 44–year–old woman with a stable, secure marriage to a wonderful, enlightened man. We have a happy blend of children from his first marriage and our marriage. To the world, it must appear as if I have the world by the tail—and I do now, after a year of therapy and some months of massage therapy at the suggestion of my therapist.

Joan did not look like she "had the world by the tail" when she entered my office the first time. An attractive person, she buried her large body in layers of clothing, bulky sweaters, and oversized pants. She was anxious and agitated and her frequent smiles seemed disconnected from what she was saying and feeling. Joan seemed well motivated to engage in what could be an emotionally painful therapeutic process as she slowly and bravely revealed her secret in that first therapy session.

> The blight of my life, the secret of secrets, was the fact that I was molested by my half–brother when I was 11 and 12 years old. The fact that I can say this now rather matter–of–factly is quite miraculous given the fact that until just a few years ago, it was only

> *a vague whisper of a nightmare haunting my subconscious mind, and yet keeping me a prisoner within myself.*
>
> *As a child I was ungrounded partly because my parents had an unhappy marriage, a hot–cold, love–hate sort of relationship that cemented my black–and–white view of the world. Never knowing whether joy or anxiety was lurking behind my own front door left me fearful and untrusting of almost everyone but my half–brother.*
>
> *My half–brother was my savior in those days of peril. He was eight years my senior, my mother's son from her first marriage, and a source of joy in my young years. When my parents were fighting, he would take me skating and I would roll away from the turmoil that left me with such great insecurities. He was my confidant and my friend, until he crossed the unspeakable line with me, the line from safe to secretive.*
>
> *With this secret came fear. Fear of telling what had happened—the possible consequence of having him removed from my life forever—the thought of that was unbearable ... he was all I had. So I lived on with this secret that was like a splinter buried deep in the skin that is forgotten until one day the whole limb is infected with the decay of this splinter, and it can no longer be ignored.*

As Joan talked with me early in her therapy, it became clear that she believed, as many survivors do, that the abuse had been her fault. It was hard for her to accept that the abuse was totally her half–brother's responsibility and that some of his apparently attentive behaviors (taking her skating, for example) might have been grooming behaviors, ways he could set her up to be grateful and dependent. With some pain and much relief, she came to accept herself as innocent in the abuse. She recognized the double bind of depending for so much emotional support on the one who abused her. She also came to understand that some of her childhood fear of telling had been a fear she would not be believed. Her fear turned out to be accurate in adult life when, while in therapy, she told her mother, who chose not to believe Joan and instead took the brother's side.

We were careful not to dissolve Joan's protective distortions before she had the ego–strength to handle it. Caution was especially warranted because the abuser was the primary stable source of any kind of attention or (even pseudo–) nurturing. The destruction of the caring illusion often precipitates deep grief. It may even potentiate suicidal thoughts and attempts with the realization that instead of there being one "sort of weird" someone who cared in *some* way, there really was *no one* at all. The client's child–self feels bereft of his or her only protection from the void. The child grieves. With the therapist's help, the adult learns to comfort the child and to reframe the child from worthless ("Nobody cared about me") to strong and worthwhile: "I survived even though I didn't get the kind of caring and nurturing I deserved. It's not my fault the adults around me were so flawed: I wasn't flawed, they were!"

> *The weight of this burden (of not telling) was quite obvious, because it was visible in the form of extra weight on my body. I had an uncontrollable compulsion for food, and that became a secret of*

its own. The extra weight became a soft suit of armor to insulate me from the pain of the outside world, and I quite literally felt trapped in my own body.

I had met and married my husband during a thinner period in my life. Thinner because of endless dieting and starving. My roller coaster food binges were only controlled with the aid of diet pills and starvation, my subconscious still keeping my secret from my conscious mind.

The years went by and I constantly fought the battle of the bulge, trying every method to cure this by–product of the secrets of my youth, while not even knowing the secrets existed.

Then one day I became consciously aware of what had happened all those many years ago. Awareness brought pain, shame, and more fear. What would happen if anyone found out? Couldn't I continue to hide it, to bury it deep within again? But it was too late. The wound had festered and exploded. It had to be resolved.

It was the Lenten season in my Episcopal church. Our rector, a gifted, dear man, spoke for three Sundays in a row about dealing with the demons within, facing the painful decisions only to walk through them to the sun on the other side. It was just too powerful for me to ignore, and I sought the name of a therapist. It turned out that therapist could not see me, but gave a strong recommendation of Dr. Robert Timms.

I felt led and at the same time driven by God as I drove to my first appointment with Dr. Timms. It was a frightening and fulfilling appointment. It was exactly what I needed. I had planned on a female therapist. I now know that I needed to deal with a man, to learn to trust another man, and not just my husband.

Through a long, painful year of therapy with Bob, I learned that I am a courageous woman with the ability to face anything that life brings my way. I have told my husband that which even he did not know, and I have confronted my brother.

Joan's desire to confront her half–brother was thoroughly discussed in therapy, and she decided to confront him when she was ready emotionally and cognitively, and at the time that felt right for her. She prepared for it in therapy, handled it very well, and was successful in communicating her feelings and thoughts to her half–brother. While the confrontation was helpful for Joan, not all survivors want or need to confront the abuser directly.

I have learned to feel anger, true unrelenting anger, and I am in the process of learning to control my weight. I am finding that stuffing food in to hold emotion down just doesn't work anymore. I am well on the road to recovery.

A few months ago, Bob suggested that I try massage therapy with Patrick Connors in order to get comfortable with the body I had hated for so many years. It was very difficult for me, and I was very skeptical of the outcome. Bob felt very strongly about it, and I agreed to try it. I can honestly say that I am increasingly successful in my quest for comfort with my body.

> *I began feeling safe enough to have my back massaged, ignoring my legs. After a few sessions, I felt comfortable enough to allow a foot massage with socks on my feet. A few sessions later the socks were off, and I wanted to try a calf massage. The first time my knees were massaged, it was very painful in a psychological way, and a physical one. Mentally, I had drawn an invisible line and anything above my knee was numb, yet powerfully painful. I spent some time in therapy discussing this phenomenon, and in the next session with Patrick the pain was gone. I am still working with Patrick, with my goal being to allow, and truly enjoy, a normal therapeutic massage, which will mean total acceptance of my body by me.*
>
> *There are some other wonderful things happening here. I am not a prisoner in my body anymore. The key to that prison evaporated along with that dark, ugly secret. I am now free to live the rest of my life without the burden of the torment of my childhood. Therapy has helped remove other obstacles also, far too many to list here, but all removed with the same result—a freedom of spirit, a sense of trust, and the richness of true self–esteem for the first time in my life.*

For Joan, memory recall was not a primary goal of either psychotherapy or bodywork. The primary goals in her psychotherapy were: to decrease fear and stress; to reassign responsibility for the abuse to the perpetrator, her half–brother; and to increase her levels of self–acceptance and self–esteem.

Patrick Connors: Bodywork was introduced into Joan's treatment program as a catalyst for discovering and focusing on the feelings she had negatively associated to different parts of her body. Once these feelings were clearly identified and connected to physical sensations, Joan could process them more effectively in therapy. This discovery, integration, and processing of emotional and kinesthetic feelings helped Joan create an ease and presence in her body that she had not known since very early in childhood and that strongly contributed to her increased self–esteem. Throughout the process, Joan regulated the pace of the bodywork, thereby reclaiming control of her body and gaining a powerful victory over the abuse.

"Paul"

Paul had been in therapy previously for about a year and remembered childhood sexual experiences with "J," an older neighbor and family friend. Paul had never defined those childhood experiences as sexual abuse (an example of denial of impact). As Paul relates, he discovered his own denial of memory (amnesia), though we were not at first aware of it. Several events brought Paul into our practice.

> *When I entered therapy with Bob two years ago, I was not aware of negative feelings toward "J," my abuser, or what he did to me. I thought of the sexual activity as pleasurable. I appreciated that he took care not to hurt me physically, and I viewed him as a strong father figure. Curiously, I had always been furious with my father, and less so with my mother, for not protecting me from "J." I*

say "curiously" because if "J" did not harm me then why would I be angry at the lack of protection? I started therapy not because I felt I had issues to deal with about the abuse but because I had just become a parent and was feeling anxious for some inexplicable reason. By anxious I mean that I feared some catastrophe was about to happen and that I would not be able to protect myself or my daughter from harm.

After several months of intense therapy, Bob and I had a therapy session with a bodyworker, Patrick Connors, in which I uncovered a memory that I had long hidden from myself. For many years, I had a gut feeling that something bad happened to me on a camping trip with "J," but I had no recollection of being on such a trip with him, so I dismissed the idea. I once mentioned my feeling to Bob who responded that he thought I might look closer to see if something did happen. I asked my father about it, and he confirmed that in fact, my father, my older brother and I once went camping with "J" and his two sons, one of whom was my best friend.

That information hit me like a bolt, and I furiously began an odyssey to discover what happened. I paid close attention to dreams that I had and images that occurred even during my waking hours.

I went again to Patrick for bodywork; he helped me identify portions of my body that were sensitive to touch. Some of my more poignant images arose during those massages. I felt frustrated—I had amassed a fair amount of images and felt pretty sure that I had been raped, but I still had no conscious memory.

This repression, the denial of fact of the rape, eventually led Paul to full amnesia (denial of memory) about the event. Yet, as for most amnesic survivors, this unconscious memory manifested itself throughout Paul's life in covert ways. One of the most frightening manifestations to Paul was the night he awakened from an unremembered dream and felt the urge to go to the bathroom. In the bathroom he discovered he was bleeding rectally. The next day he was examined by a physician, who could find no medical cause for the bleeding. This incident was one of the events that led Paul back into therapy.

Paul's report of recalling images during a massage session is typical of our client's experiences. Further, we often find bodywork increases the intensity of dreams. Paul's intensified dreams led him directly to recalling the details of the rape.

One morning, in the fall of 1988, I had a dream. In the dream, I was inside a locked gate at a public park, and was trying desperately to get out. One man and one boy in a pickup truck kept driving by, but they would not stop to help me get out. I tried pulling on the lock and I tried scaling the fence, and the gate finally began to budge. As it budged, the pickup truck drove by again and dropped a package, with postage on it, just outside the fence. I knew immediately that the package contained the bones of my dead father.

I awoke in a panic even though I knew that my father was alive and that it was just a nightmare. I couldn't calm down, and I had images flying furiously through my head. I grabbed a pen and paper to keep track of those images. As I put those images together in my head, my memory of the event kicked in. "J" did rape me on that camping trip. I had known that he wanted to do oral sex, but I asked him to wait a few minutes. He raped me to teach me a lesson about resisting him, and warned me that he would rape and kill my father if I ever resisted again, in his words, if I ever "pulled anything like that again." I was eight years old, and his anger terrified me. I started to cry. The same man who had just raped me now comforted me and told me that he didn't want to hurt me and that he in fact loved me. He kissed me and put his arms around me. I know now that he was trying to calm me down to cover his own tracks, but as a child I interpreted his compassion as loving and, on some subconscious level, I forced myself to forget that he raped me.

Reclaiming my memory has been an essential step in my recovery. Up until I remembered that rape, I was able to think of the abuse as pleasurable and benign.

Immediately after my memory came back I scheduled another session with Bob and Patrick. I was still struggling at integrating being raped into my view of the abuse as a whole, and I had to struggle to keep the memory alive and not repress it as fabricated. A combined session with Bob and Patrick helped me express for the first time a lot of my anger, and in that session I learned to see the rape as real abuse that I had not been able to stop, not as something I wanted to happen. Now that I do view the rape as part of the abuse, I see the abuse in a more rational light: "J" used me, he got cheap thrills out of overpowering me, of forcing me to submit to his sexual demands whenever he so desired. And that hurts, especially because I was a child then and I trusted him.

After I reclaimed the memory of the rape, I uncovered feelings of shame, first and foremost, then of sheer terror and anger. I also uncovered a strong desire to commit suicide that goes back to when I was a teenager and tried to kill myself by throwing myself in front of a car. It took me a long time in therapy and in a therapy group for male survivors, led by Bob and Patrick, to end my suicidal feelings and my despair.

I did not feel suicidal from that point until this past year, when I would suddenly find myself driving recklessly on the highway or fantasizing about shooting myself with a gun or hanging myself from a tree limb. When I had these thoughts I would think of how nice and peaceful it would be to be dead, to be rid of the pain and torment that has become associated with my abuse. For protection, however, I have made an agreement with myself that I will not kill myself until I have informed everyone I know of my plans—in other words, I have a fail–safe device not to do myself in.

"J's" abuse of me was such a violation that I was unable, until recently, to even consider the notion that there are people in positions of authority who I can trust, who I may even want or need to depend on during difficult times. My energies as an adult have been so often consumed by struggling to regain the autonomy that I lost as a child.

Paul's response to his new memory was like that of many survivors who recapture painful memories: "I wish it didn't happen; therefore it didn't happen: I made it up." This is a normal part of the recovery process, and represents the survivor gradually coming to terms with the full enormity of what happened.

Part of the acceptance process usually involves the client expressing his or her anger and rage over what really happened. This full knowledge leads, as it did for Paul, to a full and appropriate view of the abuse: It was done by the offender for his pleasure, and despite any messages from the abuser to the contrary, not at all for the child's benefit. Paul (or any child) is not responsible for what happened; he was used.

In a group setting, with the psychotherapist guiding the therapy, Paul was able to do some expressive bodywork with the assistance and skills of the bodyworker (a third method of using principles of the Psychophysical Model with clients). Using expressive bodywork in group therapy helped Paul face and process many of his strong emotions and suicidal feelings physically, emotionally, mentally, and spiritually with the support of his therapists and his group members.

Paul's suicidal feelings tended to recur when he was dealing with powerful therapeutic issues around anger and rage, and when he was examining his own passive or self–defeating behaviors. The old cognitive ways of blaming the self are sometimes slow to yield to more current and accurate self–perceptions. Paul persevered and often appropriately used the group setting to express his anger toward "J" and about the abuse. Now when suicidal feelings recur, he has healthier and more appropriate ways of dealing with them.

Fortunately, Paul's struggles have benefited him in many ways. He now is in a flourishing career, he has successfully confronted his abuser, and he feels free of the unfinished emotional business from his past. He is working on clarifying his relationship with his parents. He is still married, and is now the father of two children.

In our approach to therapy, the client is a full and active participant in the therapeutic process. The Psychophysical Model is done *with* the client, not *to* the client. In the following chapters, we discuss the nature of the client-therapist relationship and the therapeutic issues involved in doing bodywork and psychotherapy with abuse survivors.

7

Working Together for Healing:
The Client–Therapist Relationship

Nothing is more vital to the success of therapy with abuse survivors than the quality of the client–therapist relationship. This relationship is built on healthy professional respect for boundaries and a solid understanding of client–therapist psychological dynamics. Because of differing backgrounds and training, psychotherapists and bodyworkers initially tend to see the nature of the client–therapist relationship and the issue of boundaries differently. To use the Psychophysical Model successfully, both therapists must come to share a similar understanding of the nature of the client–therapist relationship.

The key lies in first understanding that the therapeutic relationship is a professional one with unequal power dynamics. The therapist and bodyworker are professionals who offer to provide, in exchange for payment, services that clients want, need, and agree to pay for; the relationship is economic as well as therapeutic. Emotionally, the power and the responsibility for careful, appropriate, and ethical treatment rest with the psychotherapist and the bodyworker. This relationship is even more of an issue when working with abuse survivors, many of whom feel powerless in several areas of their lives.

Whether a client has been in treatment with many different therapists for years, or is coming in for the first consultation ever, she or he will have conscious and unconscious expectations of therapy and of the therapist. While some of these expectations are spoken of, others may never be verbalized. Some expectations are clear but unrealistic. Given the years of pain and shame, repression and anxiety they have been through, it is understandable that many survivors hope for a quick cure that will allow them to "put all this behind" them. Because the trauma involves so many aspects of life and has accumulated so many layers of meaning, defense, and protection over the years, it takes time and patience to examine and heal both the injury and at least some of the emotional and psychological bruising surrounding it.

A second type of expectation is more subtle. The client may want the therapist to be a friend, or develop some kind of "special" relationship with him or her. It is the task of any therapist to help the client clarify such expectations and to address them in a healthy, nonjudgmental, and therapeutic manner. One way therapists deal with these expectations is by setting limits in therapy. The therapist is responsible for setting and maintaining appropriate limits to protect the client and allow for the safe unfolding of the therapy.

Therapists also have expectations, including some that are inappropriate. For example, a therapist may expect a client to be appreciative, "nice," or industrious, putting an unfair burden on the client. Part of a *client's* job is to test the therapist: to push limits and to behave in the ways that brought her or him into treatment in the first place. It is the *therapist's* job to meet clients where they are, and to help them grow and change. The goal of therapy is to meet appropriately the therapeutic needs of the client, not for the client to meet the needs of the therapist.

Professional supervision is one way that psychotherapists maintain clear professional boundaries. In supervision, a psychotherapist contracts with a peer or more experienced therapist to consult regularly. During consultations, the supervisor listens, asks questions, provides information, and suggests approaches for the therapist to try in working with clients. The supervisor also acts as an uninvolved third party who monitors the emotional and cognitive clarity of the therapist. The supervisor helps the therapist work through issues in therapy with clients that arise from the therapist's personal history.

In psychotherapy and related fields, much attention (some of it emotional) is currently being given to what are variously called "dual," "overlapping," or "multiple" relationships. For many practitioners and clients, the words "dual relationship" have become an emotion–laden code phrase denoting sexual contact between a therapist and client. While such contact unfortunately occurs all too frequently,[1] this narrowed use of the phrase is inaccurate and misleading.

Simply put, dual or multiple relationships are "those relationships in which different roles overlap. In one relationship, one person may have greater knowledge or power, while in another role the relationship may be more egalitarian or the power differential may be reversed" (Nevis, quoted in Chellos & Benjamin, 1992, p. 23). While this definition may seem simple, the reality of multiple relationships is complex. In general, multiple relationships may or may not be exploitive, largely depending on the character of the participants.

While most psychotherapists and counselors are trained from the beginning of graduate school to respect boundaries and to avoid multiple relationships with clients, this concept may be unfamiliar to many bodyworkers. Traditionally, many massage therapists have been people–oriented, easy–going, casual in interacting with their clients. These valuable traits naturally assist the bodyworker in helping the client to be relaxed and at ease. On the other hand, letting the complex nature of the client–therapist relationship go unrecognized creates the potential for problems. In our experience, the lack of training for bodyworkers in the importance of boundaries in the client–therapist relationship is a major gap in their professional education. This situation is beginning to change: more massage therapy schools are teaching professional

---

[1] For a review of studies on psychologists' and psychiatrists' sexual involvement with patients (suggesting as high a rate as 13.7 percent of professionals admitting to sexual contact with their patients), see Abel, Barrett, & Gardos (1992).

standards of behavior; therapists in more states are working to require licensure; and the American Massage Therapy Association is bending its efforts toward establishing clear standards of ethics and professional behavior. Still, in our experience, some massage therapists are likely to view relationships with their clients as casual and not realize the potential impact on the client of their own behaviors and attitudes.

It is the responsibility of bodyworkers and psychotherapists to establish clear and protective boundaries around the treatment, so that clients will be safe enough to experience the full healing potential of bodywork and psychotherapy. The first step in this process is for each therapist to realize that her or his function with the client is to serve as *therapist* rather than friend or colleague. It is the responsibility of each therapist to avoid inappropriate multiple relationships, for example, therapist and social friend.

As we have stated previously, any therapeutic relationship that is exploitive or sexual is inappropriate, unethical, and unacceptable. Otherwise, multiple or overlapping relationships should be evaluated on a case–by–case basis, with the primary goal being always to protect the client's safety in therapy. As Sonia Nevis, Ph.D., a psychotherapist who is a consultant and supervisor for the Muscular Therapy Institute in Cambridge, Massachusetts, says in an interview on dual relationships,

> Safety will always depend on two things being true: 1) The person with more power must not be a conscious or unconscious abuser of power; and 2) the person with less power must be old enough psychologically to be comfortable having two types of relationships with the same person. Therefore, relative safety will nearly always be easier to discern in terms of the type of people in the relationship, rather than the type of relationship. (Chellos & Benjamin, 1992, p. 30)

Any bodyworker or psychotherapist wanting to work with abuse survivors needs to examine closely his or her conscious and unconscious uses of power in relationships.[2]

It is unrealistic to pretend that multiple relationships don't exist. For example, we (Patrick and Bob) acknowledge that we have multiple relationships with each other as massage therapist and client, as business partners and colleagues, and as co–authors of this book. These relationships all work for us because we have spent time developing them appropriately and healthfully.

Therapists must learn ways to minimize the impact of multiple relationships on the therapeutic process. For example, a psychotherapist who goes to a massage therapist to experience personally the bodywork is, in a sense, in the dual roles of client and colleague with the bodyworker as the collaborative

---

[2] For an excellent discussion of the varieties and complexities of multiple relationships and a consideration of the many ethical, therapeutic, and personal issues involved, see Lerman & Porter (1990). See Appendix H for a summary of ethical and professional issues within the Psychophysical Model.

relationship begins. Two ways to minimize the impact of dual roles that are unavoidable (e.g., in small towns where a client may also be the town mechanic, the post–mistress, or a neighbor) are: 1) to allow transition time between interactions, and 2) to ensure that both roles are consciously conducted from an adult ego–state.

Therapists define the parameters or limits of the therapeutic relationship. The therapist determines how long the session will last, where sessions will take place (and for abuse survivors, this needs to be *only* at the office, *never* at the therapist's or client's home), and what the fee will be. The therapist also sets limits on how much, if any, phone contact occurs between sessions, what purpose the phone call will serve, and whether the client will be billed for phone contact.

Massage therapists may sometimes initially resist such structuring. However, when they realize that this approach provides safety and protection for a client who has had very little of either, massage therapists usually come to understand and to support this approach fully. Once the structure is in place, one has plenty of room for exploration and creativity.

Sexual abuse survivors often have never experienced adult protection. As children, they were not protected. Their emotional, psychic, and physical boundaries were violated in traumatic and disrespectful ways. Healing requires that anyone working therapeutically with survivors be very sensitive to and respectful of personal boundary issues, especially when clients are confused or unclear about their own boundaries.

At some point in treatment, clients may test the boundaries of the therapist. Many survivors were taught by childhood abusers the false lesson that all relationships are sexual and that their only value, worth, or power lies in their sexuality. Because of this learning, some survivors may flirt or otherwise sexualize the therapeutic relationship with either the psychotherapist or the bodyworker, or both. Ethical therapists do not respond in kind. In setting limits on such behavior, however, the therapist must be careful not to shame the client. A client's seductive behavior is best seen as an unconscious attempt to re–enact the abuse, hoping for a different outcome, some type of safe resolution to the original trauma. In reality, clients need therapists to be strong adults who will neither take advantage of them nor hurt them, nor allow clients in any way to hurt themselves.

It is important to tell a client directly, fairly early in the therapeutic relationship, that there will be no sexual contact between either the psychotherapist or the bodyworker and the client, within the duration of therapy or after termination. This conversation should be carefully phrased in a non-blaming, nonjudgmental way, so the client's unconscious and "internal child" can take it in and begin to learn that some adults can be fully trusted. No matter how "flirtatious" or "seductive" the client may become, the therapist sets and maintains firm boundaries of appropriate behavior that help the client reframe the perception of self in relation to others. Establishing clear sexual boundaries is particularly urgent when the therapist is the same gender as the offender.

Many adult survivors operate on the basis of childhood messages (probably all too accurate at the time, but now all too limiting) about the danger of anger; or they may be unable to distinguish anger from assertive behavior. They may fear any expression of anger, no matter how slight, whether their own or anyone else's. Survivors often believe that they will be hurt, or that if they respond with anger they will be unable to control the expression of the internal anger they feel. They may feel that their anger, if fully expressed, is strong enough to destroy everything around them. These beliefs are examples of distorted thinking that need to be clarified and resolved in therapy. The therapist and client can discuss how to allow for safety around the feeling and expression of anger; the therapist can reassure the client that the therapist will not allow behavior in therapy that would physically harm the client or anyone else.

Such agreements with the client are a form of establishing contracts. Many therapists work from a basis of setting therapeutic contracts with their clients. Contracts may be verbal or written, and may include such topics as the issues the client wants to work with, the client's therapeutic goals, and how often therapy sessions are scheduled. When necessary, the client may be asked to agree not to physically hurt herself or himself during the therapy in any way, including cutting or burning the skin and threatening or attempting suicide. The purposes of a therapeutic contract are to help clients focus on the goals of treatment and to assure their safety and protection.

Confidentiality is an issue that should be clarified between the client and both therapists. All clients have the right to know that anything they tell the therapist or that occurs during a bodywork session is kept confidential. Some abuse survivors, whose trust has been so frequently violated, have reason to fear that the therapist might talk about them to someone else. In the Psychophysical Model, we clarify for the client that the psychotherapist and the bodyworker must communicate with each other to be of maximum help to the client, but that their work with us will not be discussed with anyone else without their permission, except when a therapist seeks confidential professional supervision. We ask their permission and obtain a written release for the two therapists to communicate about the client's work and share therapeutically useful information (see Appendix D). The written permission for this communication defines a specific period of time for the sharing to occur (i.e., one month, one year). Otherwise, both bodyworker and psychotherapist agree to keep confidential anything a client does or says in the session unless the client's life or someone else's life is in danger. The only other major exception to absolute confidentiality occurs when a client discloses that she or he is sexually or physically abusing a child. Law and ethics require a therapist to report child abuse to appropriate authorities.

Being able to share information between the psychotherapist and massage therapist helps reduce the occurrence of *splitting*.[3] In the Psychophysical Model, *splitting* typically occurs when a client relates to one therapist as "the good guy" or "the good parent," and the other as "the bad parent." Commonly the client tells one therapist something negative about the other, requesting that it be kept secret: "My psychotherapist doesn't understand me," or "The bodyworker hurt my arm in the last session," followed immediately by, "but don't tell him (or her)." When this type of revelation occurs, the therapist must ask the client to discuss the issue with the other therapist, and remind the client that this secret–keeping is similar to what occurred in the dysfunctional family of origin or with the nonfamilial offender.

When psychotherapist and bodyworker have the ability to communicate with each other, secret–keeping interactions can be dealt with more directly. It may be useful at such times, for example, for the client to have a combined session with both therapists present. Accepting and valuing both positive and negative feedback from the client provide a model of honesty and nondefensive receptivity, and give the client an opportunity to claim authentic personal power. By being open to such feedback, therapists can learn from survivors, who tend to have excellent "radar" and often pick up subtle nuances or distinctions in therapists' behaviors and communications.

One necessary distinction for any persons working with abuse survivors to make is the difference between *therapy* for clients and *care–taking* of clients. While clients may wish from the depth of trauma to be "taken care of," true therapy consists of helping clients learn how to take care of themselves better, to "parent" themselves. As clients learn better self–care behaviors, they take initiative and make positive choices in their lives.

The strength of the client–therapist relationship has a direct effect on therapy with abuse survivors. Therapists can model good self–parenting by taking good care of themselves. A therapist who is always over–extended, tired, and sick is not a good model for healthy behavior, and clients probably notice this kind of nonverbal communication even more than what therapists say.

The following case study of Warren illustrates how the Psychophysical Model is applied.

"Warren"

Warren was 34 years old when he came in for psychotherapy. He had recently completed a master's degree, but did not yet have a job. He was staying home, caring for his two–year–old daughter while his wife worked full time. He had noticed that he had begun to grow increasingly angry, especially when caring for his daughter.

---

[3] While the *DSM III–R* (American Psychiatric Association, 1987) defines *splitting* as a defense mechanism "in which the person views himself or herself or others as all good or all bad, failing to integrate the positive and the negative qualities of self and others into cohesive images; often the person alternately idealizes and devalues the same person" (p. 395), we are applying the term somewhat differently because of the dynamics of the two–therapist model.

Afraid of the intensity of his anger, and fearful that he would hurt his daughter, he sought therapy. Early in his psychotherapy, it became clear that he had other issues as well, particularly about his father. There was a suggestion of childhood sexual abuse along with other emerging memories that caused him great pain.

As Warren was leaving a particularly painful session, the psychotherapist gave him what was intended as a reassuring pat on his left shoulder. When Warren came back the next week, he reported that he was furious at the therapist and that he had felt invaded by the touch on his shoulder. Since then he had been experiencing a sharp pain in the left shoulder. He said he had this pain in his shoulder before, several years ago. When he was examined at that time by a physician, no organic cause had been found, and the pain was treated by injections of cortisone that Warren had not tolerated well. He said that he did not want to try such treatment again. The psychotherapist suggested massage therapy for the pain, as well as for Warren's support during this period of emotional turmoil. Warren agreed to this suggestion.

In the psychotherapist's office, the bodyworker was introduced into the therapy process in a three–way session. Warren then told the bodyworker about his life, his psychotherapy up to that point, and the pain in his shoulder. Warren presented some information to the bodyworker that he had not previously shared with the psychotherapist and asked the bodyworker questions about how the bodywork part of the therapy would be done. When these questions were answered to his satisfaction, he made an appointment for an individual bodywork session the following week.

During the first bodywork session, the massage therapist did a general, overall body session to give Warren the opportunity to become accustomed to bodywork and to being in the massage room. This session also gave the bodyworker the opportunity to become aware of Warren's body, his tension patterns, and his muscular holding style. In later sessions, they worked more directly on Warren's left shoulder, and Warren would tighten his arm and make a fist, lock his elbow, and become flushed. He recognized that he was a little angry, but did not know what about.

In the third of the sessions that focused specifically on that shoulder, Warren had more anger, more discomfort, and more holding and resistance. At some times he felt helpless and weak; at other times he felt like struggling and fighting back. He and the bodyworker did some resistive work (pushing against the bodyworker's hands) to let Warren express and release some of the energy he was feeling. After the massage session, Warren went directly into a psychotherapy session.

In the post–bodywork psychotherapy session, Warren more clearly and directly expressed his anger verbally than ever before. The anger was less amorphous and free–floating than previously. Also, his emotional pain was more obvious in this session. It was easier for him to show emotion: he felt sad and cried.

He asked for a hug from the therapist at the end of the session, when only a few weeks before he had found invasive a touch meant to be reassuring.

Between appointments, Warren had a dream that was stirred up by the bodywork. In the dream Warren was age three or four, and he saw himself being dressed by his father in his younger sister's clothes. He was being put in a little girl's dress that was clearly too small for him, and wiggling his arm through the sleeve caused him some pain.

Kinesthetically, this memory was anchored into his body in his recurring shoulder pain. The dream was an accurate memory of a real–life event. In reality, the father had added humiliation to the physical hurt by telling Warren how "cute" he looked, like a little girl, in the dress.

Warren then was able to process the dream and the memory in his next therapy session, a combined session with both the body-worker and psychotherapist present. In two or three combined sessions Warren worked on the memory of his father dressing him in his sister's dress and of him resisting with his arm. Warren became clear that he was angry at his father, and was able to express the anger therapeutically in the sessions.

Now his present–day anger at his young daughter dissipated in the mornings when he was dressing her. He realized it was the act of putting his daughter in a dress that had triggered his now–irrational, but historically based, anger. After that part of his therapy work, Warren was able to do his parental tasks without problem or inappropriate emotion. His anger toward his father was clearly focused now, with no residual spillover to his daughter or his wife.

As Warren's example shows, everything that happens between clients and therapists is part of the therapy and can have value in the work. Warren's case illustrates several factors about the Psychophysical Model. First, the psychotherapist's well–meant touch on the shoulder was experienced by the client as intrusive and hurtful. This is an example of the psychotherapist indulging his own need to reassure the client and violating the client's boundaries by touching the client without asking permission. The client's angry reaction was appropriate, though out of proportion to the event. The level of anger indicates that the client was *transferring* anger originally felt toward his abusive father onto the therapist. However, because the two of them had developed a strong and workable therapeutic relationship, Warren was able to come back into a therapy session and speak directly to the therapist about his reactions, rather than terminating treatment.

Second, the case shows an example of the readiness of the client for bodywork and how the bodyworker is introduced to the client in the presence of the psychotherapist to help the client feel more comfortable and to bring the bodyworker into the treatment process under the "positive transferential umbrella" of the psychotherapist. That worked very well with Warren. He felt connected with the bodyworker, and set up a series of sequential sessions, first seeing the bodyworker and immediately thereafter seeing the psychotherapist.

Third, the case illustrates muscle memory as triggered by the body-work and then manifested initially in a dream. Dreams can play a significant role in therapy with abuse survivors, giving an existential message about what is happening in the client's unconscious mind. We find that the number, intensity, and significance of clients' dreams increase upon entering bodywork. Clients are usually better able to recall their dreams and share them in the therapeutic process when bodywork is part of the therapy.

The case also illustrates how the combined sessions are used to enhance therapeutic learning as well as for increased expression of emotion. Through this process, Warren gained greater knowledge and eventual healing of his family–of–origin issues, and continued to work on his experiences of emotional and physical abuse in therapy sessions. In the combined sessions, he was able to express emotions more powerfully and directly than he had been able to do in individual therapy sessions. Warren reported feeling an increased sense of help and support from working with both therapists present, and all three of us were pleased by Warren's work and progress.

Transference, Countertransference, and Projection

For a client who enters therapy to resolve old childhood issues, it sometimes starts to feel like therapy is more difficult than anticipated. Likewise, any therapist, whether dealing with emotions or the body, soon discovers that working with clients is not simple. In some therapy sessions confusing emotions and thoughts arise for both client and therapist.[4] These painful and confusing experiences generally mean therapy is working. They indicate that certain dynamics are happening in the client–therapist relationship, most frequently the dynamics of transference, countertransference, and projection.

These therapeutic dynamics may occur in any client–therapist relationship and can be magnified in the relationship between the bodyworker and the client because of the added dimension of touch. Awareness of these dynamics represents a growing edge for most bodyworkers, and full awareness and understanding of these three concepts are vital in any therapeutic relationship, particularly in work with survivors of sexual abuse.

Transference

Transference occurs when clients "transfer" certain emotions and reactions from earlier in their lives onto therapists. These emotions or reactions are often based on subtle perceptual distortions of the current situation. Transference occurs in every therapeutic relationship. Rather than trying to prevent it, effective therapy works to use transferred feelings to explore clients' histories and modes of relating. Transference can be a powerful therapeutic tool in helping clients heal their emotional wounds from the past. Many therapists believe that understanding and resolving transference feelings is a significant part of how therapy works.

---

[4] Ideally the client brings confusing emotions and thoughts back into therapy, while the therapist deals with her or his confusing emotions and thoughts in informal peer or professional supervision.

Any characteristic of the therapist, including posture, clothing, hair style, verbal style, or tone of voice, may evoke positive (or negative) transference by consciously or unconsciously reminding the client of a significant person from the past. Perhaps a Sunday school teacher patted the child on the back in a nurturing way; when a bodyworker does the same thing for the adult client, it taps a reservoir of positive feelings that originally belonged to the Sunday school teacher and that may be out of proportion to the present–day situation. Transference issues are best regarded as communiques from the survivor's past, revealing information on family dynamics and modes of communication (Courtois, 1988).

The feelings clients transfer onto their therapists can be either positive or negative. For example, a client may start to think the therapist is really terrible (a statement most therapists will not accept at face value), or may think a therapist is really great (a statement some therapists may be inclined to accept). Both varieties of transference have the potential for disrupting therapy. When both client and therapist are committed to the therapeutic process of separating the historical feelings from present feelings, they are more likely to succeed in resolving the client's historical interpersonal issues.

In our experience, most therapists are less than accurate in perceiving positive transference. For example, in positive transference, the client may see the therapist as the greatest person (or best therapist) in the whole world, with no pedestal high enough. The client may make such comments as, "You are the only person I can really talk to," or "Nobody else understands me," or "My neck has never felt better," or "I've tried everything possible to relieve my back pain, but nothing worked 'til I met you." Such positive transference may hook the therapist into losing clear therapeutic objectivity.

Everyone likes to receive recognition for his or her work, and it feels wonderful when somebody gives that recognition. While there is nothing wrong with enjoying that feeling, when a therapist starts routinely believing such transferential comments, there is trouble ahead. It is good that the client has found a therapist who works well for her or him, but in reality other therapists are equally talented and sensitive and can be just as effective with the client.

When a therapist allows positive transference to go unexplored, the client may come to feel extremely dependent on this "one person in the world" who can help. This dependence blocks the client's further growth for at least two reasons: 1) healthy growth needs to be based solidly in reality; and 2) no therapist can live up to the expectations and demands of such strong positive transference. Clients with positive transference are still giving power to someone else (the therapist), and they may engage in approval–seeking behaviors rather than finding their own power, their own center of being.

Sooner or later, clients shift their positive transferential feelings into negative ones. For example, on a day when a client is feeling especially vulnerable, needy, or upset, the therapist is seven minutes late for an appointment.

From being regarded as wonderful, kind, sensitive, insightful, and skilled, the therapist falls from grace and is now regarded as an insensitive, uncaring, greedy, oblivious, clumsy oaf. Both extremes show up in feelings that may be nominally related to a current interaction, but are out of proportion to the event.

Negative transference occurs when a client places negative feelings and perceptions from past experiences onto the therapist. These past perceptions often contain strong emotions and judgments: "You don't understand me at all!" or "I know you really don't like me!" or "You're just doing this for the money and don't care about me as a person!" The negative feelings are not directly about the therapist (or about the therapist's true feelings toward the client) any more than the positive ones are. The underlying issues are more likely to be about a parent, a spouse or partner, or some other significant person from the client's past.

While it is sometimes difficult in therapy to help a client see clearly how these past unresolved feelings continue to show up in other relationships, it is important to resolve negative transference as soon as possible. When clients are stuck in a positive transference, they still come to therapy sessions, are open and sharing, listen to the therapist's comments, and integrate what they learn into changes in their life styles. When clients are stuck in a negative transference, they may not be motivated to continue treatment.

Negative transference usually occurs at an intense point in therapy, when the client is unconsciously preparing to deal with deeper, more difficult, more painful issues. At some unconscious level, the client may be looking for a reason to avoid dealing with these issues and re–experiencing past feelings by developing a negative reaction toward the therapist. As uncomfortable as negative transference may feel to both client and therapist, with the assistance of a nonjudgmental therapist it can be the fastest way through a personal issue. The client is doing what a client is supposed to do: bring up issues from the past centered around a relationship, see these issues with the perceptual patterns learned throughout life, and recreate these patterns with the therapist in such a way as to bring about a new outcome. With the help of the therapist who responds positively or neutrally to the client in the therapeutic situation, new and clearer perceptions can emerge and healing can occur.

That's the way it's *supposed* to be. In reality, the therapist may also have a personal negative or positive response toward the client, or countertransference.

Countertransference

Countertransference occurs when the therapist has a strong or intense personal reaction to a client, based on the therapist's past personal issues. Some issues may be in direct response to the client's feelings or behaviors; others may be purely the therapist's own issues placed on the client. Therapists receive training and professional supervision to help them maintain a workable degree of therapeutic objectivity. Therapists learn that, while they may have personal feelings or reactions in their work, ideally they express their feelings only when they are therapeutic for the client, as for instance, when witnessing the therapist's genuine emotional response gives the client permission to feel his or her own emotions. Countertransference (even more so than transference) can become disruptive to the therapy and abusive to the client.

When a therapist continues to feel countertransference responses to a client, she or he needs to talk about it in consultation with a colleague, in professional supervision, or in personal therapy. Such responses need to be worked with "out loud," not merely within the therapist's mind, in order to restore some measure of compassionate objectivity to the therapeutic work with the client.

The Psychophysical Model provides some built–in help with countertransference: the two therapists serve as consultants to each other (this built–in consultation does not replace professional psychotherapeutic supervision). When one of us sees a countertransference reaction in the other, we discuss it outside the therapy session. Sometimes it may be appropriate to discuss it in the therapy session with the client to model clear communications and honest owning of inappropriate feelings or behaviors by a therapist. Since each of us has a different theoretical background, it is easier for one to question the behavior of the other, rather than both routinely following a similar theoretical path.

Positive countertransference can also lead to losing one's therapeutic objectivity. Most therapists have positive feelings about their clients. But therapists should not let strong or intense positive feelings about the client impede the therapeutic process. One example of positive countertransference might be regarding a particular client as your "favorite." Positive countertransference may motivate therapists to "bend the rules" or violate their own professional boundaries by, for example, having sessions after regular office hours or on weekends, or spending extra time in sessions. Feeling overprotective of a client is another sign of positive countertransference. Clients have contracted for the therapist's help and support in processing painful issues; for therapists to do for clients what they can and should do for themselves or to collude in avoiding the healing pain of the process is inappropriate and hinders clients' progress.

When a therapist feels sexually attracted to a client, an extremely dangerous form of "positive" countertransference is occurring. Sexual attraction to a client always indicates that a therapist needs supervision and/or personal therapy. Acting on such an attraction in any way, from flirting during sessions to developing a sexual relationship, is inappropriate and unethical, and it is dangerous and abusive to the client. Any therapist who behaves sexually with a client should be reported to his or her licensing board.

Projection

Projection occurs when a person attributes his or her own emotions or motivations to others, often unconsciously. For example, a client who did not sleep well the night before might come into a therapy session and say to the therapist, "You look tired." Projections are not usually so benign. A client may see such emotions as anger, sadness, or sexual attraction as negative and unacceptable for him or herself, and find fault with others by projecting those feelings onto them. Both clients and therapists may use projection. A good way to learn about using projection is to receive and listen to feedback from trusted friends or colleagues. Using feedback enables the projecting person to become aware of why she or he did not want to admit having such emotions or behaviors within the self and then to own them or change them.

"Mary's" case example illustrates some of these concepts.

"Mary"

Mary, married and the mother of two children, was a member of a training group focused on the use of the Psychophysical Model for survivors of sexual abuse. In the early part of the group Mary said she was afraid to do any bodywork. After spending some time in the group and watching group leaders use the Psychophysical Model with another group member, Mary formed a positive transference connection with them. She drew on those positive feelings as a support in deciding to work with the group leaders on her abuse issues, an example of how transference can be put to therapeutic use.

Mary, a large woman, felt that her weight had become a negative internal symbol of how the abuse had harmed her. She said her reluctance to use bodywork was based on her fear that anyone touching her would be repulsed by her body. Mary had internalized the thousand daily media messages that fat is repulsive, and then projected them onto the bodyworker.

As the work continued, it became clear that Mary also thought others would be repulsed if she touched them, another example of projection. To her surprise and delight, the bodyworker had no negative reactions to Mary's body and no feelings of repulsion.

Following the combined session, Mary reported feeling more alive, happier, and much more satisfied with herself. As she said, "I like me just the way I am!" Everybody in the group agreed that they liked her just the way she was, too. In a letter written a year after her experience with bodywork in the training group, Mary wrote: "I think that during our lives there are moments that become frozen in time because they are so incredibly powerful for us. Our work together was one of those moments. I remember it daily. I have grown from it. It helped me trust myself. It helped me know myself."

Mary's positive transference allowed greater therapeutic risk–taking behavior with a good result. The negative projections dissolved, leaving Mary free to be who and how she really was, with fewer judgments.

Many abuse survivors have specific somatic issues or symptoms (such as back pain, headaches, chest pain, and pelvic or genital pain), a good reason for including a bodyworker in the therapeutic process. In one kind of countertransference, a therapist or bodyworker may take on the somatic feelings or reactions of the client, both in an empathic and unconscious way. For example, a psychotherapist was working with a client who reported that whenever she remembered her childhood abuse, she felt a growing pressure inside her head until she feared her head would explode. When the client left after a very painful and emotional session, the psychotherapist realized she herself now had a feeling of intense pressure growing inside her own head. Fortunately, she had previously scheduled a massage session for herself that afternoon, and was able to use the session to explore her own feelings of abuse and hurt, and to express her emotions in a safe environment. After the session, the psychotherapist's feelings of intracranial pressure subsided. Both psychotherapy and bodywork are helpful for a therapist when she or he has a somatic response to a client's work.

Since many psychotherapists and other "helping" professionals are survivors of sexual abuse,[5] it is doubly important that any therapist who is also an abuse survivor be particularly careful and respectful of herself or himself in working with other abuse survivors. If a therapist is prone to have somatic responses to a client's issues, then the therapist needs to work on strengthening her or his own personal boundaries in ongoing personal psychotherapy.

Boundaries exist in professional work for the protection of both the client and the therapist. Nowhere is the maintenance of healthy and strong boundaries more necessary than in working therapeutically with a client whose physical, psychic, and emotional boundaries were repeatedly violated in childhood. A healthy respect for boundaries is perhaps one of the most important models therapists can provide for clients who are survivors of childhood abuse.

---

[5] A study by Pope & Feldman–Summers (1992), for example, shows that 27% of psychologists surveyed indicated they had been sexually abused in childhood by a relative, and 25% had been sexually abused by a nonfamily member.

8

Extending Embodiment: Using the Psychophysical Model With Other Client Populations

Throughout this book we have shared our ideas about how integrating bodywork and psychotherapy with adult abuse survivors leads to more effective healing from the effects of childhood sexual trauma. While the model as presented is based on individual therapy, there are also potential applications in group therapy. We have discussed this briefly in an earlier publication (Timms & Connors, 1990), and will address it in greater detail at a future point, since a full discussion of group dynamics and special principles of group therapy with abuse survivors is beyond the scope of this book (see Yalom, 1985, for a basic text on group therapy).

We also believe that the Psychophysical Model of therapy offers great promise for other client populations as well.

First, we would like to see the model adapted developmentally to work with younger persons soon after they disclose abuse. Clinical opinion generally holds that therapy initiated soon after the abuse occurs leads to faster and more integrated healing for the child, with fewer adult consequences. We would like to see the child's negative experience with touch corrected and healed as soon as possible. The integrated therapeutic approach holds the promise of increased self–approval and positive body image, and reduced anxiety and lowered possibility of distortions in perceptions of the body, self, and sexuality. A recent study on children in a psychiatric setting found that introduction of touch (through massage) into the therapeutic process lowered depression in children (Field, 1991). Since depression is a common consequence of abuse, the implications for the use of the Psychophysical Model for abused children seem obvious.

Second, the model is appropriate for adults who experienced severe childhood trauma other than sexual abuse. Physical abuse, emotional abuse, and invasive controlling religious abuse also produce negative adult consequences that respond well to this integrated therapeutic approach, as illustrated in the following case example from our practice.

Joe is a martial arts expert in his mid–30s. He has no history of sexual abuse, and was working with us to relieve his depression.

During a combined session with both bodyworker and psychotherapist present, Joe started to feel extremely angry, and wanted to
express his anger physically. We had Joe get off the massage table
and pound down onto it. His anger increased, and he started yelling
and screaming (an example of abreactive work).

He recalled and emotionally relived an event from his early 20s.
Joe had been scolding his dog without being aware of how intense
his emotions were. Meaning to spank the animal, he instead hit it so
hard that he broke the dog's back, killing his pet (while this descrip-
tion indicated that Joe was even then acting on some older, deeper
repressed emotion, we stayed with this layer of memory for that session). A neighbor heard the noise and came by the apartment as the
dog was dying. Joe, feeling guilty and ashamed of his behavior, told
the neighbor that the dog had been hit by a car, further anchoring
his guilt with a lie. As Joe recalled, expressed, and processed this
memory in a combined session, he felt the pain from that trauma,
completed the experience by releasing the guilt he had held for so
long, and forgave himself for his behavior.

In this combined session, as the bodyworker used massage
techniques to help Joe get in touch with his physical and emotional
reactions, the psychotherapist helped him track the emotions and
memories verbally. When Joe became angry and wanted to express it
(indicated by clenched fists and tense arm muscles), we encouraged
him to experience and express his anger fully in a safe, therapeutic
way. After his anger was expressed, Joe was able for the first time to
mourn the loss of his pet.

The use of these experiential expressive techniques on memories and emotions (elicited in part by bodywork) enabled Joe to dis-
charge and work through his anger in a more spontaneous and thorough way than verbal expression alone would have permitted. This
therapeutic process enabled him to tap into his deeper emotions and
memories and resolve his guilt of more than ten years. Joe's arriving
at a sense of self–forgiveness for his actions reflects a spiritual component of therapy often found when the client is fully connected,
physically and emotionally.

Joe found the combined session so powerful that after it he
wanted only combined sessions, believing that he made faster therapeutic progress that way. He once said of a combined session that
therapeutically the whole was more than the sum of the parts.

In a later combined session, Joe continued to explore his anger,
and was able to recall long–repressed memories of severe physical
abuse by his father when Joe was a child. Again, abreactive work
helped Joe express his emotions completely and safely, process
them, and integrate them therapeutically. Joe came to realize that
the disproportionate anger he felt while accidentally killing his dog
was unresolved anger toward his father. As a young child Joe was
unable to protect himself from his father or respond with anger
himself. The resulting repressed anger had manifested in many
areas of Joe's adult life. Once expressed and worked through in therapy, however, Joe was able to maintain healthier and more appropriate relationships, with both peers and authority figures.

Third, the Psychophysical Model is appropriate to consider for anyone in recovery from substance abuse or with eating disorders without a history of childhood abuse. Addictive behaviors have a cumulative effect on both the mind and the body. Bodywork applied to those in recovery offers many opportunities for help, health, and healing, and may appropriately be combined with 12-step work (Connors & Timms, 1992).

Fourth, persons suffering from chronic back pain syndrome could benefit from the Psychophysical Model. Since people with chronic pain often are depressed and frequently have a weakened or negative body image, integrated therapy could address these issues directly. Some patients with chronic pain may resist a referral for psychotherapy, with its implication that somehow the pain is not "real." The inclusion of bodywork may reconcile these patients to accepting psychotherapy to deal with feelings about their real chronic pain.

Fifth, the Psychophysical Model can be used effectively and appropriately with adults who have suffered other types of physical trauma in their adult lives. Major tragedies involving the body such as war, rape, car crashes and other accidents, severe health problems, and surgeries all leave physical and emotional memories stored in the body. These experiences may result in the development of Post–Traumatic Stress Disorder (PTSD), a diagnosis often used to describe the effects of childhood sexual abuse and characterized by strong anxiety and dissociative experiences (American Psychiatric Association, 1987, pp. 247–250). Certainly the use of bodywork for the controlled, safe release and therapeutic expression of strong emotions could play a significant part in the recovery of military veterans from PTSD. Further, appropriate use of bodywork and psychotherapy for adult rape victims (with careful attention given to the gender issues involved) could be invaluable in lowering depression and anxiety following rape, and helping the victim/survivor reclaim her or his body.[1]

Finally, any discussion of sexual violence leads inevitably to the consideration of sex offenders and their treatment. While the majority of offenders are male, a certain (and as yet unclear) percentage are females. All need treatment and rehabilitation. The reported percentage of offenders in treatment programs who were sexually abused in childhood ranges from 22 percent to 82 percent.[2] Sex offender rehabilitation programs must first work toward having the offender accept responsibility for and learn how to manage and eliminate the abusive behavior. However, at some point in sex offender treatment the therapy must also focus on the abuser's history of childhood abuse, both sexual and physical (Knopp, Freeman–Longo, & Stevenson, 1992; Knopp, 1984).

---

[1] While the use of female counselors and police in working with women rape victims is now commonly accepted as appropriate, protocols still need to be developed that recognize and address the needs and sensitivities of adult male rape victims (it is estimated that more than 500 adult males are raped per year in Atlanta alone).

[2] For a review of findings from relevant studies, see Hunter, 1990; Salter, 1988; or Knopp, 1984.

Family–of–origin issues must also be addressed therapeutically to help the offender engage in appropriate and healthy peer and family interactions in the present.

The combination of bodywork and psychotherapy could help offenders become fully aware of their bodies in a healthy and appropriate manner, develop an empathic understanding of the physical impact of their offenses on victims, and gain personal and experiential understanding of the importance of establishing and respecting personal boundaries.

We are eager for the opportunity to work more directly with offenders at an appropriate stage in their treatment progress and to work with other professionals to help develop such treatment modalities throughout the country. We believe that for sex offenders, as for their victims, fully integrated healing is possible only when both body and mind are treated and healed.

REFERENCES

Abel, G.G., Barrett, D.H., & Gardos, P.S. (1992). Sexual misconduct by physicians. *Journal of the Medical Association of Georgia, 81,* 237–246.

Abel, G.G., Mittelman, M.S., & Becker, J.V. (1983, December). The characteristics of young men who molest young children. Presentation to the World Congress of Behavior Therapy, Washington, D.C.

Alexander, F. M. (1969). *The resurrection of the body.* New York: Delta.

American Cancer Society. (1992). *Cancer facts & figures—1992.* Atlanta, GA: Author.

American Cancer Society. (1990). *Cervical cancer risk factors.* Cancer response system. Burlington, VT: Author.

American Massage Therapy Association. (1992). Code of ethics for massage therapists. *American Massage Therapy Association 1992 Membership Registry.* Chicago: Author.

American Psychiatric Association. (1987). *Diagnostic and statistical manual of mental disorders* (3rd ed. rev.). Washington, DC: Author.

American Psychological Association. (1992, December). Ethical principles of psychologists and code of conduct. *American Psychologist.*

Barlow, W. (1973). *The Alexander technique.* New York: Knopf.

Bear, E., & Dimock, P.T. (1988). *Adults molested as children: A survivor's manual for women and men.* Orwell, VT: Safer Society Press.

Bloch, J.P. (1991). *Assessment and treatment of multiple personality and dissociative disorders.* Sarasota, FL: Professional Resource.

Berne, E. (1961). *Transactional analysis in psychotherapy.* New York: Grove Press.

Bradshaw, J. (1990). *Homecoming: Reclaiming and championing your inner child.* New York: Bantam.

Briere, J. (1989). *Therapy for adults molested as children: Beyond survival.* New York: Springer.

Cawthra, S. (1992). Medical help for an alter. *S.H.A.R.E.: Support Help and Resources Exchange, 1*(2), 2–4.

Chellos, D., & Benjamin, B.E. (1992). Dual roles and other ethical considerations. *Massage Therapy Journal,* Spring, 22–32.

Connors, P., & Timms, R.J. (1992). Bodywork: An aid to recovery. *The Recovery Network, 1*(1), 7–8.

Cornell, W., & Olio, K.A. (1991). Integrating affect in treatment with adult survivors of physical and sexual abuse. *American Journal of Orthopsychiatry, 61*(1), 59–69.

Courtois, C.A. (1988). *Healing the incest wound: Adult survivors in therapy.* New York: W.W. Norton.

Cousins, N. (1989). *Head first: The biology of hope.* New York: Dutton.

Crewdson, J. (1988). *By silence betrayed: Sexual abuse of children in America.* Boston: Little, Brown.

Durrell, L. (1976). Introduction. In G. Groddeck, *The book of the it* (pp. v–xxx). New York: International Universities Press. (Originally published in 1949).

Dychtwald, K. (1986). *Bodymind.* Los Angeles: Tarcher. (Originally published in 1977, Pantheon).

Feldenkreis, M. (1970). *Body and mature behavior.* New York: International Universities Press. (Originally published in 1949).

Field, T. (1991). A new dimension in intensive care. *Massage Therapy Journal, 30*(3), 50–60.

Finkelhor, D. (1984). *Child sexual abuse: New theory & research.* New York: Free Press/Macmillan.

Freud, S. (1950). *The ego and the id.* London: Hogarth Press.

Groddeck, G. (1976). *The book of the it.* (V. M. E. Collins, Trans.). New York: International Universities Press. (Originally published in 1923).

Heckler, R.S. (1984). *The anatomy of change: East/west approaches to body/mind therapy.* Boston: Shambhala.

Heller, J., & Henkin, W. (1986). *Bodywise.* Los Angeles: Tarcher.

Hindman, J. (1989). *Just before dawn.* Ontario, OR: AlexAndria Associates.

Hocking, S.J., & Company. (1992). *Living with yourselves: A survival manual for people with multiple personalities.* Rockville, MD: Launch.

Hunter, M. (1990). *The sexually abused male: Prevalence, impact and treatment* (Vol. 1). Lexington, MA: Lexington Books.

Jacobson, E. (1938). *Progressive relaxation.* Chicago: University of Chicago Press.

Jones, F.P. (1976). *Body awareness in action: A study of the Alexander technique.* New York: Schocken.

Juhan, D. (1987). *Job's body: A handbook for bodywork.* Barrytown, NY: Station Hill Press.

Keleman, S. (1979). *Somatic reality.* Berkeley, CA: Center Press.

Kepner, J.I. (1987). *Body process.* New York: Gardner.

Kluft, R.P. (1984). Treatment of multiple personality disorder. In B.G. Braun (Ed.), *The Psychiatric Clinics of North America, 7*(1), Symposium on Multiple Personality. Philadelphia: W. B. Saunders.

Knopp, F.H. (1984). *Retraining adult sex offenders: Methods and models.* Orwell, VT: Safer Society Press.

Knopp, F.H., Freeman–Longo, R., & Stevenson, W.F. (1992). *Nationwide survey of juvenile & adult sex offender treatment programs & models, 1992.* Orwell, VT: Safer Society Press.

Kreisman, J.J., & Straus, H. (1989). *I hate you—don't leave me: Understanding the borderline personality.* New York: Avon.

Kurtz, R. (1990). *Body–centered psychotherapy: The Hakomi method.* Mendocino, CA: LifeRhythm.

Kurtz, R., & Prestera, H. (1976). *The body reveals.* New York: Harper & Row.

Lerman, H., & Porter, N. (Eds.). (1990). *Feminist ethics in psychotherapy.* New York: Springer.

Lowen, A. (1958). *Physical dynamics of character structure: Bodily form and movement in analytic therapy.* New York: Grune & Stratton.

Lowen, A. (1975). *Bioenergetics.* New York: Coward, McCann & Geoghegan.

Marcus, E.H. (1979). *Gestalt therapy and beyond: An integrated mind–body approach.* Cupertino, CA: META.

Masson, J.M. (1984). *The assault on truth: Freud's suppression of the seduction theory.* New York: Farrar, Straus & Giroux.

McCann, I.L., & Pearlman, L.A. (1990). *Psychological trauma and the adult survivor: Theory, therapy, and transformation.* New York: Brunner/Mazel.

Miller, K.J. (1991, November). *The prevalence of childhood sexual abuse among women with eating disorders.* Paper presented at the Renfrew Foundation conference, "Intergenerational Issues of Women with Eating Disorders," Philadelphia, PA.

Montague, A. (1971). *Touching: The human significance of the skin.* New York: Harper & Row.

National Task Force on Juvenile Sexual Offending. (1988). Preliminary report of the national task force on juvenile sexual offending, 1988. *Juvenile Family Court Journal, 39*(2), 8.

Perls, F., Hefferline, R.F., & Goodman, P. (1951). *Gestalt therapy: Excitement and growth in the human personality.* New York: Julian Press.

Pert, C.B. (1986). The wisdom of the receptors: Neuropeptides, the emotions, and bodymind. *Advances 3,* 8–16.

Pert, C.B., Ruff, M.R., Weber, R.J., & Herkenham, M. (1985). Neuropeptides and their receptors: A psychosomatic network. *Journal of Immunology, 135,* 820s–826s.

Pope, K.S., & Feldman–Summers, S. (1992). National survey of psychologists' sexual & physical abuse history and their evaluation of training and competence in these areas. *Professional Psychology: Research and Practice, 23*(5), 353–361.

Putnam, F.W. (1989). *Diagnosis and treatment of multiple personality disorder.* New York: Guilford.

Reich, W. (1972). *Character analysis* (3rd ed.). (V. R. Carfagno, Trans.). New York: Farrar, Straus & Giroux. (Originally published in 1933, 3rd ed., first published in 1949).

Reiser, M. (1984). *Mind, brain, body.* New York: Basic Books.

Reiser, M. (1990). *Memory in mind and brain.* New York: Basic Books.

Rosenberg, J., Rand, M., & Asay, D. (1989). *Body, self, and soul: Sustaining integration.* Atlanta: Humanics Limited.

Rolf, I.P. (1989). *Rolfing.* Rochester, VT: Healing Arts Press. (Originally published in 1977).

Salter, A.C. (1988). *Treating child sex offenders and victims: A practical guide.* Newbury Park, CA: Sage.

Smith, E.W.L. (1985). *The body in psychotherapy.* Jefferson, NC: McFarland.

Thomas, T. (1990). *Surviving with serenity.* Deerfield Beach, FL: Health Communications.

Timms, R.J., & Connors, P. (1990). Integrating psychotherapy and bodywork for abuse survivors: A psychophysical model. In M. Hunter (Ed.), *The sexually abused male: Application of treatment strategies,* (Vol. 2, pp. 117–136). Lexington, MA: Lexington Books.

Timms, R.J., & Connors, P. (1992). Adult promiscuity following childhood sexual abuse: An introduction. *The Psychotherapy Patient, 8*(1/2), 19–28.

Yalom, I.D. (1985). *The theory and practice of group psychotherapy* (3rd ed.). New York: Basic Books.

Appendix A

For Clients:
Choosing a Therapist for
Child Sexual Abuse Issues*

With all the choices of therapists in your community, finding the right one for you or your child can be very difficult. Not all therapists are qualified in the area of child sexual abuse. It is up to you to interview potential therapists and make a careful decision. You, as an individual and a consumer, should obtain information about your therapist's qualifications, therapeutic background, and treatment philosophy.

In choosing the right therapist, it is important to consider your own values, attitudes, and feelings. Therapists may be from various disciplines: social work, psychology, counseling, psychiatry, or other associated fields. Each will approach therapy and the treatment of sexual abuse issues based on their own unique blend of experience, training, theoretical orientation, and individual personality.

The following gives you information about how to get started in finding a therapist and also provides a list of questions to ask. This is not intended to cover every question you might have. You may want to add your own questions to the list provided, and you should not feel bound to ask all of these questions.

Developing a List of Therapists

The first thing you could do to start your search is to narrow your choices to two or three. If you have no idea who to call, look through the telephone yellow pages under the following headings: "Social Workers," "Psychologists," "Psychiatrists," "Marriage and Family Counselors," Psychotherapists," or any other mental–health related field. See if anyone lists sexual abuse as their specialty.

Or, contact one of your social service or mental health agencies and request the names of competent sexual abuse therapists.

If transportation is a problem, you may need to narrow your search to a specific geographical area.

When you call therapists, tell them you are in the process of choosing a therapist to help with your particular problem. Inform them that you have a number of questions that will take some time to answer. Ask if they are willing to answer the question and whether a fee will be charged for that time. You may be able to do some preliminary screening if the therapist is willing to answer some of the questions over the phone.

---

* Reprinted with permission from the author, Carlos Loredo, Ph.D., Austin, Texas.

Review the checklist and be familiar with the questions before you see any of the therapists. If you have been referred to a particular therapist, review the checklist anyway. You might want to write the answers on a separate piece of paper if you contact more than one therapist. It would be helpful to make appointments with at least two therapists so you can compare their responses. Be aware that most therapist will ask you for information pertaining to the sexual abuse and your particular needs and expectations, so be prepared to answer some questions yourself.

Interviewing the Therapists

Experience and training:

— What academic degrees and/or other recognition or general training and experience do you have?
— Are you licensed or certified by a board? Which one?
— How many years of experience in providing therapy have you had?
— What internships or special training in sexual abuse have you had? Where and when? How long?
— Have you attended or conducted any sexual abuse workshops? If so, when and where?
— How many sexual abuse cases have you treated per year? How many are you currently treating?
— Do you specialize in any area of sexual abuse?
— Have you provided testimony in a court of law as a sexual abuse expert? How many times?
— How much experience have you had working with gays/lesbians? What is your philosophy about homosexuality?
— Do you deal with anything other than sexual abuse in your practice? What types of cases?
— Do you have supervision/consultation available to you?
— What kinds of clients do you typically see?
    Offender/victim
    Adults/children/teenagers
    Men/women
    Women/rape
    Sexual innuendo (sexual harassment, etc.)
    Other
— What is the age range of children you serve?
— What is the age preference for your clients?
— Familiarity and relationship with the community

Ask the therapists what kind of community contact they have. Feel free to contact community agencies or other resources to see if they have heard of the therapist or have any information to give you about them.

Ask the therapists to provide three references in the community (or other locale where she or he has practiced) or persons you can contact who are familiar with their work in sexual abuse.

Ask the therapists if a complaint has ever been filed against them, or with their certification/licensing board. If so, why, and what was the outcome?

Fees

You have the right to ask these questions of the therapists. They are extremely important to your therapy.

— How much is your fee?
— Do you have a sliding fee scale? If so what is the range?
— What are your billing and payment policies?
— Do you accept third–party (insurance) payments?
— Do you accept Victim Compensation payments?
— Do you accept alternate forms of payment (bartering, monthly payments)?
— Do you charge for a cancellation or "no show"?
— Do you charge for telephone consultations?
— What are your fees for the services offered?

        Evaluation reports:
        Expert testimony:
        Consultation:
        Testing:
        Type of treatment:
        Court preparation:
        Billing–related:
        Other:

— Are any of these items negotiable?

Treatment Issues

— Basically you will need to know from the therapist:

        What are we going to do?
        How are we going to do it?
        How long will it take?
        What do we hope to accomplish?
        How will we know when we've accomplished it?

— Are there any eligibility requirements or type of cases you will not take?
— What are your typical working hours? Weekends? Evenings? Do you provide crisis intervention?
— How many other cases like mine have you treated?
— Do you maintain written progress notes? Will I have access to those notes?

— Will you provide written reports and progress summaries?
— What is your policy regarding confidentiality?
— How often, for how long, and with whom will you meet?
— Do you ever leave your office to provide services (for instance, home or school visits)?
— Would you report your clients if they physically or sexually abused children? (The correct answer is "yes".)
— Will you testify in court, if necessary? If so, are you willing to state a clear opinion and make specific recommendations?

Making the Decision

After each interview make notes as soon as possible about your impressions of the therapist; if you interview more than one therapist, you may forget. In making the decision, consider these issues:
— How did the therapist respond to your questions and your needs?
— What was your reaction to the therapist?
  • Consider your own personal biases, values, and attitudes (religious preference, culture/ethnicity, feminist philosophy, role of advocacy, sexual preference, views regarding homosexuality).
  • Consider your special needs (for example, if you have problems with alcohol, drug abuse, or violence, etc., the therapist should be experienced in those areas).
— How did this therapist compare with the other(s) you interviewed?
Note: If your health plan does not provide coverage for a specialist in this area, you have the right to demand the care you need.

After You Have Been in Therapy Several Weeks, Consider How You Feel About Your Therapist:

— Are you intimidated by your therapist?
— Does your therapist listen to you?
— Do you feel you can disagree with your therapist?
— How does your therapist handle crisis and conflict?

At no point are you "stuck" with a particular therapist. If your own particular needs are not being met, you have the right to find another therapist more suitable to you. It is a good idea, however, to discuss your dissatisfaction with your therapist before terminating therapy.

Unfortunately, there are therapists who act sexually suggestive or otherwise victimize clients. If this happens to you, immediately report the therapist to his/her board and find another therapist.

Appendix B

For Clients:
Guidelines for Choosing a Bodyworker

One way to start is with word–of–mouth referrals. Talk to friends and other people you trust to see if they have ever received therapeutic massage. Learn what you can from the experiences of others.

Then begin to interview bodyworkers. Ask questions about their training and background, such as: Do they have experience in working with persons in recovery? How long have they been doing this work? Do they have any past or present clients who would be willing to serve as references? It is important to note here that while confidentially has been promised by any legitimate massage therapist doing this work, some clients are willing, even eager, to share their experience with others if it will be of help. For clients who have given their permission there is no breach of confidentiality; they can be an exceptionally valuable resource for those seeking the right therapist.

Ask directly what the bodyworker or massage therapist charges, how long an appointment lasts, and whether the bodyworker has an office with other professionals or works alone. Find out the therapist's policy on clothing and draping during the session if that is a concern for you. Whatever concerns you have are legitimate topics for discussion during the interview. Listen not only to the words she or he responds with but also listen for his or her feeling tone. Does the therapist seem patient, safe, and understanding of your needs?

Because a particular bodyworker worked well for a friend of yours does not necessarily mean she or he will be "right" for you. This is a very personal and intimate form of therapy. The component of touch can magnify or intensify certain issues and dynamics. Only work with someone you feel right about. We believe the rapport between the client and therapist to be the most important factor in reaching therapeutic goals. It is much more important than any particular style or technique of bodywork used.

We believe that the gender of the bodyworker is relatively unimportant compared to the energy or feeling she or he projects.

The bodyworker must be well–grounded in the principles of the client–therapist relationship and well informed about the dynamics of transference, countertransference, projection, denial, and dissociation. We believe the bodyworker must be comfortable with a wide range of emotions in himself or herself to work effectively with a variety of emotions in others.

We suggest the bodyworker have some knowledge of and sensitivity to the concept of the "inner child" and the role its wounds play in the recovery process. Sometimes during therapy the "adult" part of us will make some agreement or contract that the inner child has not agreed to. Complications arise if at some point during the session the adult ego–state dissociates and leaves only the inner child state present in an unfamiliar situation. The bodyworker needs to recognize when this is happening, reassure the child ego-state, and find ways to call back the adult ego–state.

There are two national professional organizations for massage therapists and/or bodyworkers: The American Massage Therapy Association and The Association of Professional Massage Therapists. Membership in either of these two organizations increases the likelihood (but does not guarantee) that the therapist you are interviewing is sufficiently trained and experienced to meet your needs.

Appendix C

For Clients: What to Expect From Bodywork

In a Professional Bodywork Session, You Can Expect:

— a professional environment and approach.

— a "safe" place in which to work, as you define safe.

— to be treated with respect, both verbally and nonverbally.

— to give the bodyworker appropriate information about your physical and medical health and history.

— to give information about your previous experience, if any, with therapeutic massage.

— to set goals for your therapy.

— to be listened to carefully, and not be criticized.

— to be accepted where and as you are, without judgment.

— to make your own decision about whether to remove any clothing, and if so, how much.

— the bodyworker to leave the room when you are getting dressed and undressed.

— to be always appropriately covered with a sheet, except for the part of your body being worked on.

— to have total control over how much physical pressure the bodyworker uses (i.e., safe touch).

— to be able to stop the bodywork at any time and discuss it.

— neither to be flattered nor criticized about your body.

— never to be touched on your breasts or genitals.

— to talk or not talk during the session, as you choose.

— the possibility that a wide range of emotions may surface, with or without specific content.

As Treatment Continues Over Time, You Can Expect:

— to experience therapeutic touch as safe, nurturing, and healing.

— an increase in physical pleasure in life and a decrease in pain.

— improved body image and self-esteem, and a diminished sense of shame.

— improved integration of body, mind, emotions, and spirit.

— increased awareness of and appropriate expression of physical and emotional needs.

— to improve communication between your emotional and physical experience. For example, when an emotion occurs, with corresponding physical cues, you can learn to read what is happening sooner, even at the time, rather than figure it out an hour, a day, or a week later.

— that as you become more at peace with your body, you will become more at peace with your thoughts and feelings.

— to reclaim disconnected parts of your body, and perhaps to reclaim disconnected parts of your memory.

— to re-evaluate your sense of body boundaries. They may be reinforced for clearer or more time-appropriate reasons, or they may be restructured so as to be a better match for where you are presently in your growth and recovery.

Appendix D

Authorization to Release Information

I, _____ hereby authorize
(printed name of client)

_____ to discuss any details of my
(printed name of therapist)

condition and treatment, or to release written information about same to:

_____ _____

_____

_____

     This authorization is good for one year from the date signed, unless revoked in writing earlier. A copy of this authorization will be legally acceptable. I agree to release and hold free from harm the therapist and agency for any use that the person or institution to whom the information is released may make of it. I understand the nature of this form, and have discussed it with my therapist before signing.

_____   _____
(signature of client)   (date signed)

_____   _____
(witness signature)   (date signed)

Appendix E

Brief Confidential Medical History Form

Name _____   Home Phone _____
Address _____   Work Phone _____
_____   State _____ Zip _____
City _____   Date of Birth _____
Referred by _____

Present Symptom: What is your major reason for wanting massage therapy?

_____
_____
_____

Minor Complaints: Other areas of pain or concern? _____

_____

When did you first notice major complaint? _____
What brought it on? _____
What aggravates this condition? _____
Is this condition progressively getting worse? ___ Yes ___ No
                                                ___ Constant ___ Comes and goes
Is this condition interfering with your work?___ Yes ___ Sleep? ___ Daily Routine?
What have you done to get relief? _____
Has there been a medical diagnosis? _____ If yes, what was the diagnosis? ___

_____

By whom? _____   Address _____
Have you ever had any operations? ___ Yes ___ No Describe: _____

_____

Broken any bones? ___ Yes ___ No Describe: _____

_____

Been in an accident? ___ Yes ___ No Describe: _____

_____

If yes, did you receive a whiplash? _____
Do you have any history of seizures? _____
Have you had any other serious injuries? _____

_____

Habits:	Heavy	Moderate	Light	None
Alcohol	_____	_____	_____	_____
Coffee/Tea	_____	_____	_____	_____
Soda	_____	_____	_____	_____
Tobacco	_____	_____	_____	_____
Exercise	_____	_____	_____	_____
Weekly Sugar Consumption	_____	_____	_____	_____

Do you have difficulty with the following:

- ❏ Headaches
- ❏ Migraines
- ❏ Light–headedness
- ❏ Loss of memory
- ❏ Eye problems
- ❏ Ringing in ears
- ❏ Dizziness
- ❏ Sinus trouble
- ❏ Asthma
- ❏ TMJ dysfunction
- ❏ Dental braces
- ❏ Throat infections
- ❏ Throat constrictions
- ❏ Twitching of face
- ❏ Whiplash
- ❏ Spinal cord problems
- ❏ Slipped disk
- ❏ Pinched nerves in back

- ❏ Chest pains
- ❏ High blood pressure
- ❏ Low blood pressure
- ❏ Irregular heartbeat
- ❏ Heart attack
- ❏ Shortness of breath
- ❏ Pins and needles in arms and hands
- ❏ Cold hands
- ❏ Digestion problems
- ❏ Ulcers
- ❏ Anemia
- ❏ Liver trouble
- ❏ Gall bladder trouble
- ❏ Bladder trouble
- ❏ Kidney trouble
- ❏ Stomach trouble
- ❏ Constipation
- ❏ Diminished sex drive

- ❏ PMS
- ❏ Painful menstrual cramps
- ❏ Complications giving birth
- ❏ Pins and needles in legs and feet
- ❏ Cold feet
- ❏ Skin allergies
- ❏ Painful or swollen joints
- ❏ Arthritis
- ❏ Insomnia
- ❏ Nightmares
- ❏ Inner tension
- ❏ Irritability
- ❏ Nerves and nervousness
- ❏ Depression
- ❏ Chronic fatigue

Do you have any other medical condition or physical limitation that I need to be aware of before you receive massage therapy? ___ Yes ___ No
If yes, describe: _____
_____
_____

   Because a massage therapist must be aware of any existing physical conditions that I have, I have listed all my known medical conditions and physical limitations and I will inform the massage therapist in writing of any change in my physical health.

   I understand that the massage therapy that I am given is for the purpose of stress reduction, relief from muscular tension or spasm, and/or for improving circulation. I understand that a massage therapist neither diagnoses illness, disease, or any other medical, physical, or mental disorder; nor performs any spinal manipulations. I am responsible for consulting a qualified physician for any physical ailment that I have.

   I agree to pay for all services at the time they are rendered unless prior arrangements have been made.

_____   _____
Signature   Date

Appendix F

For Psychotherapists:
Guidelines for Choosing a Bodyworker

Begin with reading and implementing the suggestions for clients looking for a bodyworker (Appendix B). Some additional suggestions and considerations are listed below.

How to Start a Search

1. Ask colleagues and abuse survivor clients whom they use.
2. Check with local or regional massage schools for referrals; be specific in your request.
3. Check with the Atlanta Center for Integrative Therapy (20 Executive Park West, Suite 2025, Atlanta, GA, 30329 / phone 404–321–5533) for possible referrals to bodyworkers in your area who have attended our trainings.

What to Look For

1. Both a male and a female bodyworker experienced in working with abuse survivors.
2. Either a certified or a licensed massage therapist or other bodywork professional, depending on the laws in your state (not all states license massage therapists or bodyworkers).
3. A therapist willing to collaborate in the team approach.
4. Clear and appropriate ethical and professional standards; understanding of boundary issues.
5. Sensitivity to gender–related issues.
6. An appropriate, private, and safe office space.

Evaluation of Bodyworker

1. Set up an appointment and receive a massage (expect to pay for this session: you are buying a service).

2. Interview the bodyworker before and after the massage. Be clear about your needs and expectations.
3. Evaluate the impact of the bodyworker's personal and professional style; give feedback. If you have any concerns, now is the time to share them.

If all goes well, discuss with the bodyworker the model proposed in this book, sharing a copy with her or him. Be open about your style of working, any expectations you have for working together, and specific client–therapist relationship issues you want the bodyworker to be aware of. Good luck in your work together.

Appendix G

A Summary of Benefits of the Psychophysical Model

1. Recalling of repressed or amnesic traumatic memories.

2. Increased ability of client to differentiate between remembered pain and present–day pain.

3. Increased awareness and appropriate expression of emotions.

4. Facilitation of acceptance by adult ego–state of child ego–state's pain, thus helping with self–nurturing. Splits in the client are relieved by integrating adult ego functions with child ego experiences and emotions.

5. Enhanced congruence between internal experiences and external behaviors.

6. Breaking of old patterns of passive behavior and moving into new and appropriate risk–taking and growth ventures.

7. Decrease or elimination of shame, self–blame, and inappropriate feelings of guilt.

8. Improvement in body image and self–esteem.

9. Increased relaxation, decreased stress, and improved health.

10. Integration of client's past and present, thus allowing for a more healthy future.

Appendix H

A Summary of Ethical and Professional Issues in the Psychophysical Model

It is vital in doing either bodywork or psychotherapy with abuse survivors that both therapists follow professional guidelines for ethical behavior. These guidelines include the following:

1. Each professional therapist recognizes and works within the appropriate limits of his or her professional competence.
2. The privacy and confidentiality of the patient is always respected. Permission is obtained in writing from the client for the two therapists to discuss the client's case with each other and within professional supervision sessions.
3. There is no sexual contact or sexual behavior, either explicit or implicit, between the therapist and client, inside or outside of the therapy setting.
4. Each therapist gives highest consideration to the needs of the client, and also to the needs of the profession.
5. Each therapist is aware of the nature of "dual" or "multiple" roles and avoids them when they might harm the client. NOTE: This must be recognized as a complex issue that may require consultation or supervision.

Other professional issues include being aware of the dynamics of abuse survivors by attending training workshops, extensive reading, and obtaining clinical supervision. Whenever a therapist recognizes difficulties in therapy, she or he seeks peer or professional supervision. If necessary, she or he also seeks personal psychotherapy.

It is vital for both therapists to recognize and understand the importance of the therapist–client relationship, with all its attendant dynamics including transference, countertransference, projection, distortion, and denial.

In the Psychophysical Model it is the role of the psychotherapist to advise the bodyworker when the client is diagnosed with any personality disorder (Borderline Personality Disorder, for example) that may require extra care or precautions in therapy. The psychotherapist should also advise the bodyworker of abuse survivor's degree of dissociation.

It is the role of the bodyworker (having previously solicited and received the client's written permission to consult) to advise the psychotherapist of pertinent material that surfaces in the bodywork session (some clients may not be able to report their experiences accurately since they may be somewhat dissociated).

Neither therapist lets a client who is in a highly dissociated state leave the office. Rather, therapeutic steps are taken to decrease the dissociation and return the client to a functioning adult–ego state. It is important that both psychotherapist and bodyworker know how to help the client do this.

About the Authors

PATRICK CONNORS, C.M.T., is a massage therapist who has been specializing in work with survivors of sexual and/or physical abuse since 1987. A graduate of the Atlanta School of Massage, Patrick is a member and officer in the Georgia Chapter of the American Massage Therapy Association. He is also an instructor in Neuromuscular Therapy and co–teaches (with Robert Timms) a class in somatic psychology at Oglethorpe University in Atlanta. Patrick is a cofounder of the Atlanta Center for Integrative Therapy and codeveloper of the Psychophysical Model. He has been leading workshops nationally since 1988 and has been published extensively.

ROBERT TIMMS, Ph.D., is a clinical psychologist and psychotherapist. A member of many professional associations, Robert is a Fellow of the Georgia Psychological Association and has been recognized by the American Group Psychotherapy Association as a Master Instructor in group therapy. He is adjunct faculty at Oglethorpe University in Atlanta. Working extensively with both male and female abuse survivors, Robert concentrates on group work and professional training. With Patrick Connors he is a codeveloper of the Psychophysical Model of Therapy. Robert has published extensively on somatic psychology, sexuality, and sexual abuse, and has led more than 300 professional and client workshops around the country.

The Safer Society Program, a nonprofit project of the New York State Council of Churches, is a national research, advocacy and referral center on the prevention of sexual abuse. It serves as an informal clearinghouse/network center for newly emerging topics related to those issues. The Safer Society Program and Press publish relevant research, studies and books that contribute to the development of sexual victim and offender treatment as well as to primary prevention.